92
Gou

22,609

Gould, Charles N.
Covered wagon geologist

DATE DUE			
APR 3 '85			
MAY 27 1991			
APR 26 1994			
MAY 27 1997			
SEP 13 1999			
SEP 3 8 2002			
APR 14 2004			
APR 8 2011			

HANSFORD COUNTY LIBRARY
SPEARMAN, TEXAS

Covered Wagon Geologist

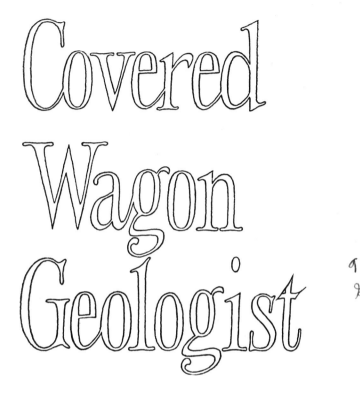

Covered Wagon Geologist

CHARLES N. GOULD

92
Dou

22,609

NORMAN : UNIVERSITY OF OKLAHOMA PRESS

LIBRARY OF CONGRESS CATALOG CARD NUMBER 59-7954

Copyright 1959 by the University of Oklahoma Press, Publishing Division of the University. Composed and printed at Norman, Oklahoma, U.S.A., by the University of Oklahoma Press. First edition.

INTRODUCTION

CHARLES N. GOULD occupies a unique and significant place in American geology. His professional career, which spanned almost sixty years, is a rich one, distinguished for its pioneering accomplishments in the geology and paleontology of the Southwest. He was not only a scientist but a teacher, consultant, public servant, and benefactor of many.

Born in a log cabin on an Ohio farm near Duck Creek (in July, 1868), reared in a dugout on the prairies of Kansas, he was inspired one summer evening by a lecture, "The Geological Story of Kansas," while preparing for a career as a country school teacher. From that experience came his determination to become a geologist. Although he has been dead for more than a decade, it is clear that Charles N. Gould's career greatly influenced, not only professional geologists, but men and women in many other walks of life. In a covered wagon, in a buckboard, on foot, on horseback and finally by automobile, he pursued geology in many areas of the Southwest.

Looking back in 1946 upon his more than half a century of service to the people of the region and his profession as a teacher of geology at the University of Oklahoma, as organizer and director of the Geological Survey of the state, and as consulting geologist and National Park geologist, he could justly claim to have participated in the development of his profession from its covered wagon days to its maturity at mid-twentieth century.

v

His autobiography, here published for the first time, has been printed almost without change, to keep his record as it was in 1946, three years before his death. I have made no effort to bring it up to date by the addition of editorial notes, nor have I gone back of 1946 to account in such notes for the comings and goings, the changes of title, or the deaths of men whom Charles N. Gould knew and who had shared his interests and won distinction in his time in science, teaching, and exploration. To have done so would have required constant heckling of the text, which is unnecessary for those who are professional geologists and merely distracting to the large audience of general readers awaiting the publication of this memorable bit of history.

It is only fair to comment on one somewhat controversial item which I am sure Charles Gould would want done if he and I could talk about it today: the circumstances leading to the discovery of the Augusta, Kansas, Oil Field. Notes from Gould's files, in his own handwriting, dated December 2, 1946, show that he first examined the area about 1912, found a large anticline, made a sketchy reconnaissance map, and recommended leasing the area. As a result, several thousand acres of leases were acquired on the anticline along a strip twelve miles long and two miles wide.

Two field parties were sent to map the area with plane table, alidade, and rod, one of the earliest instances in the Mid-Continent where a prospect was mapped and a contour map prepared in advance of the drill. This map was under supervision of Everett Carpenter, Gould's brother-in-law and former student, who had been a member of the United States Geological Survey. Actual detailed preparation of the map was carried out by Roy Hazelton and Russell Crabtree, well-known names to geologists. Gould and Carpenter then recommended drilling, and a discovery well resulted which opened the prolific Augusta

Field. The credit for this discovery must be divided, part to Gould for recognizing a favorable prospect, and part to Carpenter for the precise work finally leading to the discovery.

Those of us who are actively engaged in the practice of geology in the Southwest know that Charlie Gould's autobiography is far from a comprehensive statement of his accomplishments during a long and fruitful career. The scientific side of the story, contained in 260 papers, 572 reports on oil properties, and 251 geological reports made for the National Park Service, might be assumed to provide an ample supplement. But even this does not complete the picture, nor do the written tributes paid to him after his death reciting his memberships in learned societies and his honorary degrees and memberships, both at home and abroad. A great modern building, housing the School of Geology at the University of Oklahoma, Charles Newton Gould Hall, stands as a tribute to the man who laid the foundation for the school having the largest enrollment of any of its kind in the world today. The careers of his former students and associates in the survey are monumental to his achievements. Among these are DeGolyer, Belt, Denison, Ferguson, Keyes, Gouin, Buttram, Monnett, Newby, Kirk, Reeds, Schramm, Tomlinson, and Clifton, to mention only a few. These pages tell only indirectly of his tolerance, subtle wit, kindliness, modesty, and dedication to, and interest in, young people aspiring to careers in geology.

Charlie Gould was Mr. Geology of Oklahoma or, more accurately, Mr. Geology of the Southwest. Among geologists of this area of middle age or older, many of them his former pupils, friends, and associates, are memories of principles and discoveries, major and minor, from the geological explorations by their old preceptor, friend, and mentor, which collectively make up the legend of Charlie Gould.

He was somewhat diffident about, and perhaps a bit careless or even unimpressed by, the importance and interest of some of his findings to his contemporaries and those who followed him. In his autobiography, for example, nothing is said about Gould's pioneer and fundamental work in the Permian Red Beds of western Oklahoma, or the significance of the buried mountain range in western Oklahoma and the Texas Panhandle. This buried westward extension of the Wichita Mountains, the site of the prolific Texas Panhandle Oil and Gas Field, with its vast millions of barrels of oil and great quantities of gas, has had profound economic importance for the entire region.

Pure science was always Gould's abiding interest. One of his friends, after reading some of the chapters of this autobiography, once asked him why he did not point out the ultimate significance of his purely scientific work to the economic development of the mineral resources (specifically oil) of the Southwest. He answered very frankly, "I hate oil geology."

But there may have been an overt reason for his dislike of the money side of his profession. Although his financial rewards in commercial work were adequate, wealth eluded him. He drilled, in areas he firmly believed to be underlain by oil deposits, a number of dusters. Although he failed to find oil production, he was not wrong. On these very prospects, the sites of his earlier failures, subsequent development proved prolific production in zones below the depths to which he and his associates had drilled. It was a sad experience for a man who had successfully pioneered so much oil territory for others, either incidentally and without recompense or as a geological consultant for modest fees. If this was indeed a reason for his ignoring many significant details in his productive career, as they subsequently affected mineral developments, he never said so.

Charlie Gould's writings often reveal a wistful quality and approach to humans and their vicissitudes for which one may find analogues in the writings of Eugene Manlove Rhodes.

Although he speaks of Rhodes only once in this book, he had developed a great fondness and affinity for him, not as a personal acquaintance, but as a kindred spirit. For this, the evidence is plain. Gould had read everything he could find of Rhodes's—short stories, novelettes, articles, and novels. And the deep affection of the master storyteller for the landscape and the lonely figures upon it finds its counterpart in the wanderings of the geologist, on foot, on horseback, by covered wagon and buckboard, and finally by automobile.

He shared with Rhodes the quality of simplicity and the ability to get things straight on paper. During his periods as director of the Oklahoma Geological Survey, he wrote hundreds of news releases about survey activities. In them he revealed these literary assets. The limited editorial marks for capitalization, punctuation, spelling, and usage on his manuscript, as it appears on my desk after being marked for typesetting by the staff of the University of Oklahoma Press, afford ample evidence that not only was Gould a notable geologist, but a good writer and editor as well. And his retelling of the old nester's adventure story confirms his reputation as a much better than average spinner of yarns.

And why did Charlie Gould's contribution to the history of the Southwest, *Covered Wagon Geologist*, fail to achieve publication in the period from 1946 to 1949, the year of his death? Members of the staff of the University of Oklahoma Press read the manuscript in 1946 and suggested that he include more of his "explorations of the subsurface," with which he was so justly credited. He was thought to be making these revisions, but he apparently lost the zest for additional writing as the years grew upon him (he was 81 when he died at Norman, Oklahoma, August 13, 1949), or, perhaps more likely, he simply thought such revisions unimportant and unnecessary to his story.

The manuscript remained unpublished until the summer of

1958, when I rediscovered it. The Oklahoma City Geological Society conducted a field conference over the scenes of many of Gould's early explorations in the Texas and Oklahoma panhandles in the fall of 1958. The resulting guide book was dedicated to Charles N. Gould. His son, Donald Boyd Gould, also a geologist, was one of the lecturers and honored guests of the conference. As a result of many conferences with Don, I was allowed to read the manuscript. I read it in my hotel during the watches of one summer night with amazement and fascination. It was no problem to convince the Oklahoma City Geological Society that this story was not only an important contribution to the geology but to the history of the Southwest and should be printed. The project was discussed with a number of Gould's former students, friends, and associates from all parts of the country, many of whom subsequently read the manuscript. The encouragement and assistance of these fellow geologists (among whom are some of America's most distinguished scientists) made possible the publication of these notable memoirs.

To C. W. Tomlinson, A. I. Levorsen, R. L. Keyes, R. L. Clifton, C. H. Taylor, Dean A. McGee, Everett Carpenter, Frank Gouin, J. V. Howell, C. Don Hughes, John Ferguson, Elisha A. Paschal, Jerry B. Newby, R. W. Loughlin, K. A. Ellison, Roy D. McAninich, Harold D. Jenkins, J. R. McGehee, W. J. Hilseweck, Frank E. Lewis, and Mildred and John Frizzell, I am most grateful for counsel, encouragement, and assistance.

Through a unity of purpose and a determination to see this "last testament" of Charles N. Gould to completion, this book now results from the combined efforts of those individuals, the Oklahoma City Geological Society, and the University of Oklahoma Press.

B. W. BEEBE

Oklahoma City, Oklahoma
February 9, 1959

CONTENTS

xi

ILLUSTRATIONS

Covered Wagon Geologist

CHAPTER 1

THE OLD HOME IN OHIO

IT WAS A HOT AUGUST NIGHT in 1889. Some fifty country boys and girls, prospective school teachers, were seated in a stuffy schoolroom in Kingman, Kansas, listening to a lecture on the geology of Kansas. The girls all wore bustles and most of the boys had sandburs in their trousers.

This was during the summer Normal Institute, which in those days was held in each Kansas county for the training of teachers.

The speaker was L. C. Wooster, the conductor of the institute. He had gone down to the banks of the Ninnescah River, which flows through Kingman, and had picked up two slabs of red sandstone, each about an inch thick. These he held up before us so that we might see that on one slab there were ripple marks, and on the other mud cracks.

Professor Wooster explained to us simply but clearly that these slabs were once part of a sea beach. He told us that the ripple marks were formed by the action of waves on the sand, just as ripple marks were being produced along the banks of the Ninnescah today, and that if we would go down to the river we might see mud cracks very similar to those on the slab he was holding up before us.

He explained that at the time when these sandstones were being deposited the greater part of Kansas, as well as much of North America, was an open sea, and that at that time neither the Rocky Mountains nor the Appalachian Mountains were in

3

existence. He said that the same forces of nature—wind, rain, running water, heat, cold, and chemical agencies which we could see today—have been active throughout all geologic time, and that by these agencies our world is still being shaped. He gave us the foundation stone of the science of geology, viz., "All rocks have been laid down under water," and explained that by great convulsions of nature mountains were raised, and then by the processes of erosion these mountains were again worn down.

I hung entranced on every word. As Professor Wooster continued his lecture unfolding nature's handiwork, I felt the spinal shiver which betokens the last word in emotional appeal. This was my conversion.

Up to that time, I do not believe that I had heard the word geology spoken. I may have run across the word in my reading, but it certainly had no place either in my vocabulary or in my thinking.

This lecture changed the entire current of my life. At that time I did not know what a geologist did, but I then and there resolved that whatever things a geologist did, those things must I do. I then and there resolved that, in as much as in me lay, I would devote my life to learning how the rocks had been laid down and how they had been all mussed up.

And now for nearly a decade more than half a century I have constantly kept before my eyes the resolution made that hot August night.

My earliest childhood recollection is of a broken-down wagon, an old spring house, and a willow tree. I fell off the wagon, rolled down the steps by the spring house, lodged against the tree and howled. Mother ran out, picked me up, and comforted me. This must have been before I was three years old, for Mother told me we moved from this place a few weeks before my third birthday.

4

The log cabin where I was born was on a hillside on Grand-father Robinson's farm, in southern Noble County, Ohio. The little town where we did our trading was Lower Salem, in northern Washington County, three and one-half miles away.

Southeastern Ohio was settled largely by immigrants from the older states. My father's people, the Goulds, were of old Massachusetts Yankee Puritan stock. I am the ninth in direct descent from Zaccheus Gould, who, with his family, emigrated from England in 1638, eighteen years after the coming of the Mayflower. He settled at Topsfield, near Lynn, north of Boston, where members of the family still live.

Soon after the Revolutionary War, my great grandfather, Benjamin Gould, then a young man, came with his father, Nathan, from Massachusetts to Virginia. Benjamin Gould moved from Virginia to southeastern Ohio in 1808, and entered land along Duck Creek, sixteen miles north of Marietta, the first settlement in Northwest Territory. I have the parchment signed by James Monroe conveying to him a tract of land, the old farm on Duck Creek. To this farm Benjamin brought his wife, Lydia Alden, a descendant of John and Priscilla Alden. Here they raised a family and here they died and were buried.

Grandfather Ephraim Gould, whom I remember as an old man, lived and died on this farm. He, too, was buried in the little cemetery at Gould's Church, which was located on the old farm. Ephraim was a man with strong convictions. He was an abolitionist and kept a station on the underground railroad, over which Negro slaves, escaping from Virginia, were passed from one station to another until they reached Canada. He served as county commissioner, was an ardent prohibitionist and a member of the Washingtonians, the first temperance society organized in Ohio. His wife, Lois Porter Gould, died many years before I was born. My father, Simon Gilbert, born in 1842, was the eighth of eleven children.

5

My mother's maiden name was Anna Arvilla Robinson. In 1824, Grandfather Caleb Robinson, a Quaker, with his wife, Catherine, and five small children, set out in an ox-drawn covered wagon from Maryland to found a home in the wilderness. They finally settled on a tract of eighty acres of hilly, forest land in southeastern Ohio. There they built a log house on a hillside, near a spring, and there they raised a family and grew to old age, and there they died. My mother, born on this farm in 1842, was the youngest of fourteen children.

During nearly sixty years of happy married life in Ohio, my grandmother never saw a town of more than two thousand people. She carried all the water for cooking and household use up a slippery path from the spring. She cooked over a wood fire in an old-fashioned fireplace, in an iron pot and a Dutch oven. Fire was kept overnight by covering the coals with wood ashes. If by chance the fire died, it was necessary to get a shovelful of coals from a neighbor. Among her kitchen utensils were wooden bowls, earthenware crocks, and pewter spoons. The drinking gourd hung on a nail by the water bucket. She carded wool and flax, spun it into yarn, colored the yarn with vegetable dyes—oak galls for black, hickory and butternut bark for yellow, and walnut hulls for brown—wove the yarn into cloth on a hand loom, and with a needle sewed the cloth into clothing for all the family.

The family slept on feather beds filled with feathers from geese raised on the farm. The covering was woven coverlets, counterpanes, or patchwork quilts. When any of the family took a journey, they went in a lumber wagon, on horseback, or afoot. If two went on horseback, they either rode double or traveled "ride and tie," which meant that the first man would ride ahead, and at some agreed place would tie the horse and start walking. The second man came up to the horse, untied it, mounted, overtook and passed the first man. Farther along the

6

road he would tie the horse and start on afoot. And so, alternately walking and riding the men would reach their destination.

Grandmother raised a garden of vegetables to supply the table, and a posy bed for beauty. Tomatoes, called "love apples," were raised in the posy bed as curiosities but were not eaten, since they were thought to be poisonous. There was an herb bed, with catnip, sage, parsley, horehound, and lavender for medicinal and household use. Mint and pennyroyal grew wild.

With the ax, Grandfather Robinson and his sons cleared the forest. They cut down the trees, split clapboards to cover the buildings and rails to fence the fields, supplied wood for the fireplace, and disposed of the excess logs by piling them in great heaps to be burned. Corn and potatoes were planted by hand and covered and cultivated with a hoe. Grain was cut with a sickle or a cradle, gathered with a long handled rake, tied into bundles with bands of twisted straw, placed in shocks, threshed with a flail or by tramping out with horses, and winnowed in a windmill. Wheat was carried to a gristmill on horseback. Cattle were butchered for beef and the hides tanned into leather. Grandfather made the shoes for the family and harness for the horses. He was his own carpenter and blacksmith. Hemp raised on the farm was twisted into rope.

Grandmother saved wood ashes from the fire and piled them into an ash-hopper in the back yard, poured water into the hopper to make lye, and this lye was boiled with grease in a big iron kettle to make soap. There were two kinds—soft soap for scrubbing floors and hard soap for scrubbing hands. Tallow candles furnished light. In the spring, my grandfather tapped the native sugar maple trees, collected the sap in buckets, boiled it in kettles to make syrup and sugar for household use. Fruit was raised in the orchard and blackberries and raspberries picked from wild briars. Sassafras roots were dug from the ground and the bark used for tea.

7

Practically everything the family ate and wore was produced on the farm. Salt, soda, coffee, and tea were obtained at the country store, not by payment of cash, for of cash there was little, but by barter of butter, eggs, and other farm produce.

My parents were married December 3, 1864, near the close of the Civil War. There were twin boys, Herbert and Herman, three years older than I, but both died in infancy, and were buried in the same little grave in the cemetery at Gould's Church. I was born on July 22, 1868, in the little log house by a spring under the hill, on Grandfather Robinson's farm.

After mother's death in 1920, we found, among her papers, the following note:

"One hot sultry morning in July, 1868, in Eastern Ohio, on the waters of Duck Creek, in a little log cabin, with clapboard roof, and open fire-place; with chimney of mud and sticks, in the primitive style of the early settlers of that country, a baby boy was born. His parents were poor, having scarcely the comforts of life; for weeks they would live on the most meager fare of corn bread and fat meat without an atom of wheat bread or sugar. On that morning after the baby came, the father went to a neighbor and bought a few pounds of flour that the occasion might be duly celebrated with a mess of warm biscuit for dinner. The mother, sick in bed, saw them, for the cooking and eating were all done in the one room of the house in which she lay, and wanted one of them so badly, but the attending physician, true to the old-time superstition, said, 'No, they will not be good for you.'

"As time went on the little fellow grew and prospered in spite of his environments and semi-poverty. Not a healthy child, for he had many hard and severe spells of sickness and several times we despaired of his life; but bright and active. As most boys in very early childhood he had a passion for reading, and would sit for hours and listen to his mother read stories from such story books as she had at command, and especially stories from the Bible, until he became familiar with all the characters of the Bible, and other simple books as well. He improved every opportunity within his reach to gain an education, and worked in the meantime to earn money to buy his clothes and books.

"At twenty years of age, after the family came to Kansas, he taught his first country school for four months at thirty dollars per month, paying ten dollars per month for board. His first twenty dollars was spent for a suit of clothes complete, hat, and shoes, of which he was greatly in need. He followed teaching for a number of years, giving his wages to his parents and to his sister, who was six years younger than he."

Evidently Mother had written more, but if so, it has been lost.

The house where I was born has been torn down for many years, but Mother described it to me as having one room, with a rough board floor, and a knothole down which little Charley would poke things, one door and one window, an old-fashioned stone fireplace, and a loft overhead reached by a ladder. It was located over a hill from Grandfather Robinson's house. In 1931, in company with Jim Rhodes and Allen Whetstone, two boyhood friends, I visited the site of this house. We found only a pile of stones that marked the location of the old chimney, and the spring from which Mother carried water.

When I was five, the family moved to Grandfather Gould's farm. Grandfather was growing old. He measured off twenty acres from the corner of his farm, and deeded it to Father. On this tract Father built a two-room house with an attic, shaded by a large beech tree. I well remember moving into this unfinished house. Later two more rooms and a porch were added and two attic rooms were finished. In this new house, my

9

sister Minnie Rose was born. About this time Grandfather was stricken with paralysis and lay bedridden until his death seven years later.

The part of the state in which we lived is typical of southeastern Ohio. The country is hilly, almost mountainous, with narrow creek valleys, and is much cut up with small streams, ridges, and hollows. The hills are steep and were originally covered with timber. At the time of my earliest recollections, the greater part of the best timberland had been cleared, and only the steeper and more inaccessible hillsides retained their native trees.

Roads were dusty in summer and muddy in winter. Often for weeks at a time, during the fall and spring months, they were practically impassable because of mud and water.

Grandfather Gould was an ardent Methodist and had been a church steward for more than forty years. His house was the itinerant Methodist preacher's home. He gave the land upon which the church was built, also the land for the cemetery, and for the schoolhouse. The church was known locally as "Gould's Church," or sometimes as "Mount Ephraim."

The social life of the community centered around the church. There was preaching by the circuit rider every two weeks, class meeting on alternate Sundays, and Sunday school every Sabbath morning. Every winter a revival meeting was held and the whole community attended. During one of these meetings, when I was fourteen years old, I joined the Methodist Episcopal Church. For a number of years I was sexton, and rang the church bell, swept, dusted, carried coal, built fires, tended the lamps, and looked after the church. For this I was promised the "munificent" sum of one dollar a month.

I started to school when I was six and went through McGuffey's readers, Ray's arithmetic, and Harvey's grammar, and, until my eighteenth year my school experience was that of the ordinary country boy. I could solve all the problems in Ray's third part arithmetic, and even ventured in Ray's higher. I could parse and diagram most of the sentences in Harvey's grammar, and knew the Eclectic geography from cover to cover. Geography was always my favorite study. Arithmetic was difficult, grammar uninteresting, but I excelled in geography.

The twenty-acre farm upon which we lived lay mostly on the hillside with a deep hollow, or "run," passing through it. At the time of my first remembrance, the greater part of the farm was yet in timber, consisting of a heavy growth of beech, oak, poplar, elm, sugar maple, and other hardwoods of the Ohio Valley. For a number of years Father cleared out a few acres each year, the work usually being done during the winter. He would chop down the trees, saving any portion that was suitable for saw logs, pile the brush and burn it. The ground under some of the largest brush piles was utilized as tobacco beds, where we raised the young plants, which afterwards were transplanted into the field. The next spring the land would be planted to either corn or tobacco. It fell to my lot, much against my inclination, to hoe these crops, and keep them free from weeds.

The steep hillsides were plowed with an old-fashioned double-moldboard plow by beginning at the bottom of the hill and working back and forth, turning the plow over at the end of each furrow. We had two faithful farm horses, Jenny and Filly, and usually one or two cows. Mother raised chickens, and there were always several hogs on the farm. After cold weather came in the fall, two or three fat hogs were butchered for our winter meat.

Coal is abundant in southern Ohio. Father had on his farm a coal bank where he dug coal and hauled it to supply the neighbors. For several years he marketed it at Lower Salem. As I grew older, I helped in the digging and hauling. Coal was sold by the bushel, and Father received three cents a bushel at

11

the farm and seven cents in Lower Salem. Father also frequently engaged in teaming for the neighbors, particularly in hauling lumber from the local sawmills to the little towns or to the railroad.

Both Father and Mother were hard-working, economical, and painstaking people all their lives. I once heard Father say that except when we sold the farm to move to Kansas, he never had at one time as much as fifty dollars in cash.

Life on the farm was rather primitive. We were past the first stage of the pioneers; the loom and spinning wheel had been relegated to the attic, but much of the food and clothing was still raised on the farm and prepared at home. A few of the older women still spun yarn and wove cloth. I remember pouring melted tallow into molds to make candles, and pouring melted lead into molds to make bullets. The rag wick in the lard dish often served as a lamp. We had one kerosene lamp of which Mother was very much afraid, because she feared it would explode and set the house on fire. We children were never permitted to handle the lamp.

Much of the labor was done as a community enterprise. Such things as barn-raisings and grubbings by the men, and quiltings and carpet-rag-sewings by the women, were often neighborhood affairs. We boys attended all these gatherings, anxious to help, but the men usually chased us away, insisting that we were a nuisance and did more harm than good.

In the raising of a barn, the large beams and timbers that were to go into the frame had been squared with a broad ax, so that all that was needed was to lift them into place. The beams were pushed or slid up long skids by men with poles, and fitted into place by other men working on the building. In clearing a piece of new ground for cultivation, the men with axes and grubbing hoes worked ahead, chopping down the large trees and saplings, trimming them up, and grubbing out the smaller brush and sprouts by the roots. We boys followed behind collecting the brush and heaping it into piles to be burned.

In the meantime the women had been busy in the kitchen. A long table had been set in the living room, loaded with all sorts of good things to eat: meats, including baked ham, chicken, and mutton, vegetables, three kinds of bread, preserves, pickles, jams, jellies, and a variety of pies and cakes. Many of these things were rarely on our table at home. At noon the hard-working men first satisfied their hunger, and we boys ate second table. In the afternoon the women and girls quilted or sewed carpet rags.

The only instance I ever remember when my father bought tobacco was at the time of the barn raising on our farm. It was customary to treat the men to cigars. I've always thought that it hurt his conscience, not because he begrudged the money, but because he was opposed to smoking.

At harvest and threshing time, the men exchanged work. A threshing machine, run by horse power, would move from farm to farm, and the neighborhood men did the work about the machine. From the time I was fourteen years old, I usually worked on the stack, and became quite expert in building a symmetrical straw stack. Father had taught me the stacker's motto, "Keep the middle well tramped."

Mother once inherited a small amount of money from her mother's estate, with which she bought a sewing machine with a foot treadle, the first one in our neighborhood. Until that time, following the universal custom, she had made all the clothing for the family by hand. The sewing machine created quite a sensation and the women dropped in to see it work, while several of them brought material for garments and learned to run it.

Public opinion was divided. Many of the women thought it was a good thing and would save a lot of time. Others, the more conservative, did not approve. One dear old sister, not noticing a little boy standing near, said, "Mark my word, Arvilla will be sorry, taking up with all those new-fangled contraptions. Why can't she be satisfied to do her sewin' like the rest of us have always done?"

I had one pair of boots per year, bought in the fall and made to last through the winter. There were no rights and lefts, and Father saw to it that I changed over each morning on the theory that the boots would wear longer. In summer all the boys and girls went barefoot. Under the stairway hung the boot jack, which Father and I used at night for pulling off our water-soaked boots. In the yard stood a grindstone, and it was Charley's job to turn the stone while Father sharpened his ax or scythe. Of all farm chores, I think I disliked most turning the grindstone.

Wheat and corn were raised on the farm, taken to the Boye water mill near Lower Salem, and ground into flour or meal. This was a famous fishing place, and I was always anxious to go to mill to try my luck while the grain was being ground. In shelling the corn for grinding, we sometimes borrowed a corn sheller, but more often a wash tub full of ears of yellow corn would be brought into the living room after supper, and, by the light of the coal fire in the grate, the entire family would fall to and shell the corn by hand.

Our food was plain but plentiful, chiefly the produce of the farm. At our home, corn in its various forms was a staple article of diet. My favorite food was always "roasting ears" or green corn on the cob. Apparently I could never get enough, for Father used to ration us, "Eight ears of corn for old Jenny, and six for Charley."

And mush and milk! How I enjoyed it, and do yet. To my mind, no better, more wholesome or more palatable food ever graced an American table. For supper yellow cornmeal mush, well-cooked, with fresh sweet milk; and for breakfast fried mush, with butter and homemade sorghum molasses. How many stalwart American families have been raised on such a diet!

But no more. We have gone soft and effeminate. Nowadays we have for breakfast some sort of "cereal," a tasteless, insipid, unpalatable, over-advertised, expensive concoction bought at the grocery store which we pour out of a paper box and swallow under protest because it's the proper thing to do. The American people are the unconscious victims of multitudinous advertising campaigns paid for by a few milling companies.

On the farm buckwheat cakes were a favorite food on winter mornings. Along in the fall Mother would start a jar of buckwheat batter, containing yeast, which was kept on the top shelf of the pantry. From this jar she would dip out batter for the hot griddle, and to it from time to time she would add more brown buckwheat flour. Salt pork was on the table the year around. Butter and eggs produced on the farm were either sold at the local store or exchanged for sugar, coffee, tea, salt, and spices.

In fact, with us, eggs were not considered food but commodities. Only once a year, on Easter Sunday, were we children permitted to eat eggs. For two weeks before Easter we all followed the established custom of hiding eggs. Competition was keen as to who could hide the most eggs. For Easter breakfast, we were allowed to eat all the eggs we could hold. And again competition ran high. One of my chums claimed to have eaten eight eggs for breakfast, while I had eaten only six. Somehow I never have enjoyed being beaten at any game, so next year I planned to retrieve my shattered reputation.

We had a little brown hen named Betsy, part bantam, that laid a very small egg. I sorted out Betsy's eggs and gave twelve of them to Mother to fry for my Sunday breakfast. The dozen eggs made a full meal; but, after having eaten them, I felt that I could still do a little better, so I had Mother cook one more egg. I ate half of it, making twelve and one-half eggs.

Before Sunday School, the boys were all recounting their gastronomic achievements; one boy had eaten seven eggs, another nine. I kept quiet, saying never a word. Finally Clyde Hallet spoke up, "Charley, how many eggs did you eat this morning?" Nonchalantly I replied, "A dozen and a half." The boys were nonplussed. They didn't believe the story. One of them hunted up Mother and said, "Mrs. Gould, how many eggs did Charley really eat for breakfast?" Again, as always, Mother was a good sport. "Why, Charley ate a dozen and a half this morning," she answered.

Nearly sixty years later on a visit to the old home in Ohio, I heard the Easter-egg story repeated.

Mother always raised a good garden. Queerly enough, although I detested work in the field, the garden work was not irksome. In the fall the vegetables were stored in "holes"; there was usually a potato hole, a turnip hole, an apple hole, and a cabbage hole. The vegetables were dumped in a long pile on a bed of wheat straw on the ground, and covered with a layer of straw and a foot or more of dirt to prevent freezing. Many is the time that Mother sent me out with a dishpan or a crock to get a mess of potatoes or turnips for dinner.

Mother's flower garden brightened a strip of front yard. This garden included many old-time perennials, together with groups of her favorite annuals. I remember the fragrant early-blooming pink roses. Then there were stately tiger lilies, modest bleeding-hearts and violets, gay flowering almonds, bouncing bets and ragged robins, together with low clumps of bright green live-forever; while pansies, marigolds, zinnias, petunias, and asters filled extra spaces with color and beauty. When we later went to Kansas we found growing wild several flowers, including spiderwort, coreopsis, snow-on-the-mountain, and sunflowers, which in Ohio had been raised in gardens.

There was a row of currant bushes along the path to the barn, and cherry, apple, and quince trees in the yard. A large Concord grapevine almost covered the south end of the house. When the fruit was ripe, I could lean out of an upstairs window and pick large bunches of the purple grapes.

A number of wild fruits grew in our neighborhood, including pawpaws, persimmons, black haws, mulberries, May apples, wild grapes, and June berries (or "sarvice" berries, which in Canada are called Saskatoons). When pawpaw bushes produced their fruit in the late summer, Mother would take my sister and me to the thicket, where we picked and ate the soft, luscious fruit, or, if the pawpaws were not quite ripe, we would bring them home and lay them in the sun to ripen. In the early summer we would gather May apples, or mandrake fruit, from the low, spreading plant with the yellowish-green fruit hidden in a bunch of leaves.

Mulberries and June berries grew on larger trees. As the forests were cleared, farmers had saved the fruit-bearing trees. They often stood solitary in the pastures and plowed fields. Every boy in the neighborhood knew where these trees were, and we watched eagerly for the ripening of the fruit, although we were sometimes chased out of the trees by their indignant owners.

After the first frost in the fall, the persimmons and wild grapes would ripen, and we would go with baskets and pails and bring home the fruit. From the wild grapes, Mother made jelly and top-spreading for our school lunches.

I did not eat a banana until I was fifteen, and never saw canned goods in a store until after I left Ohio. On festive occasions, such as Christmas or the Fourth of July, the children would be given perhaps half an orange each. The peel would be laid away on the top shelf of the cupboard to dry, to be enjoyed a month later. Lemonade and ice cream were never known except at country picnics. Theatres were unknown and circuses were considered immoral. Perhaps once a year a magic-lantern show would come to the schoolhouse, and at the close of school an exhibition was usually given. Sports were almost unheard of. There was an old swimming pool under a high bank by a sycamore tree, on Duck Creek, and occasionally I could obtain permission to go swimming with the boys, but I fear that sometimes I slipped off without my parents' knowledge. In one sport only did I excel. I could usually beat the other boys at ice skating.

During the noon intermission and recess at school, we played the ordinary boyish games, such as town ball, blackman, and hide-and-seek. When snow was on the ground, the boys brought sleds and coasted down the hill back of the schoolhouse. Such games as checkers, authors, and the like, while not forbidden, were not encouraged. Trashy novels, cheap story papers, and playing cards were not permitted in the house. The Sabbath was strictly observed, and on this day few games might be played and the studying of school books was not permitted.

Family worship was observed daily. Just before breakfast, the family would gather in the living room and Father would read a chapter from the Bible and lead in prayer, all members of the family kneeling. Grace was always said before meals. To us, religious observance was a vital thing and part of our daily lives.

When I was yet a little boy, seven or eight years old, Mother subscribed to *The Youth's Companion* for me, and I read it eagerly for many years. Many a time I have cut short my dinner in order to finish a *Companion* story before going into the field. To this paper I owe much of my early education and the desire to accomplish something in life. Our library contained but few books, and those largely of a religious nature. I distinctly remember poring for long hours over *Clark's Commentaries on the Scriptures*, which Mother bought when she was fifteen years old. This set of books is still in my library.

Fishing was fairly good in Duck Creek, and often after the day's work was done, I would dig worms for bait and go down to the creek and fish until after dark, usually bringing home a string of catfish, suckers, and perch, which Mother cooked for breakfast next morning. Sometimes several of the neighbor boys would come and we would build a fire and stay out until ten o'clock. Occasionally I brought in a soft-shelled turtle and Mother would make turtle soup.

The Goulds always had pets on the farm. The dog, Bark, whom I trained to bring up the cows, later went with us to Kansas, riding in the baggage car. Our cats had distinctive names like Beelzebub, called Zebub for short, Tiglath-phileser, Ramesses II, Zadok, and Abimalech. Even the little pigs and chickens had names.

When I was thirteen, I bought a cheap, single-barrel, muzzle-loading shotgun, and from that time on, took every opportunity to "go hunting." Rabbits were plentiful and squirrels were occasionally found in the timber. There were a few foxes, raccoons, and opossums in the country, but I was never successful in capturing any of this larger game.

In the autumn we always gathered nuts. Walnuts and butternuts grew on our farm, and one of my chores was hulling the former. My hands would be stained black for weeks with the juice from the hulls. We picked hickory nuts "on the shares" from a neighbor's farm, and by permission gathered chestnuts from other farms. When my sister and I made a trip back to the old neighborhood in 1940, we found that a blight had killed all the chestnut trees.

In the winter, spelling schools were common. Half a dozen

of us country boys would tramp several miles over the hills to a schoolhouse to attend the spelling school, conducted on the old-fashioned plan of two captains choosing up and each side trying to spell down the other side. From the time I was fifteen, I was counted a fairly good speller, and I still have an autograph album which I received as a prize for being one of the champion spellers of Salem township.

Mother said that from the time I was a little boy I was always making collections of smooth pebbles and curious rocks. The window ledges were filled with rock specimens. One of my chief amusements was digging in the dirt banks and exploring caves and ravines on the hillsides. I certainly would never have made a success as a farmer, for I thoroughly disliked farm work. I detested doing chores. I gradually attained the reputation of being the laziest boy in the neighborhood, and this fact is still remembered on Duck Creek. The first work I ever did off my Father's farm was gathering bundles in a neighbor's wheat field. For a day's work, I received what to me, then, was the large sum of twenty-five cents.

My sister Minnie Rose, six years younger than I, shared in my boyish sports. We walked on stilts, climbed the beech tree, and went fishing, hunting and nutting together. From the time that she was a little tot, not large enough to go to school, I always had the idea that I should watch over and protect her.

We were poor, much poorer than many of the children in the neighborhood, but our parents had the good sense never to let us get the idea that we were poor. I remember reading in *The Youth's Companion*, and such papers as came into our hands, of poor children, and how I used to pity them, not realizing that we, ourselves, were as poor as they. My sister and I often remark upon the fact that Mother never permitted us to know that we were poor. There were always school books at the time school opened, and clothes and shoes ready for us. At Christmas time there was candy in the stockings, and maybe a toy, a doll, a story book, a cap or a pair of mittens. Mother has told me that when my baby sister was only about one year old, I went alone to the store and selected the calico for a dress for her, paying for it with nickels and pennies that I had saved.

Mother was a leader among the women and children in our neighborhood. I remember that she and Mrs. Mary Hallett organized and maintained for the children a temperance society called "The Band of Hope." This little society met once a week, and we children were instructed in matters of neatness, politeness, temperance, and "general culture." We signed the pledge, promising "to abstain from the use of all alcoholic liquors, including wine, beer, and cider as a beverage, and to discourage their use by others." This early temperance teaching impressed me greatly and never since have I ever been able to look with any degree of tolerance upon the liquor traffic, nor any of its attendant evils. Today I do not know the taste of spirituous liquor, nor have I ever used tobacco in any form.

The Band of Hope held annual picnics in the Hallett's beech grove. At one of these picnics, I recited Joseph Rodman Drake's patriotic poem beginning:

"When Freedom from her mountain height unfurled her
    standard to the air,
"She tore the azure robe of night, and set the stars of
    Glory there."

I find, after an interval of nearly sixty years, I can still recite from memory the greater part of the poem.

Mother always believed, and made us believe, that we could do the work that was to be done. Her encouragement was unlimited. She trusted us and oftentimes, simply by her faith in our ability, we were willing to undertake and eventually were able to overcome many difficult tasks. "Be on time" and "Be dependable" were two of Mother's precepts.

She used to tell the story of the boy who went with a crowd of children picking berries. While the rest of the boys and girls were running from bush to bush, each trying to get the largest and finest fruit, this little fellow stuck resolutely to a single bush until it was finished. Then he went to the next and completed it, and so on throughout the day. When night came his basket was full, but the baskets of the children who had spent their time running all over the field contained few berries. The moral was: "Stick to your bush," and Mother used to impress this precept on us so thoroughly that neither my sister nor I have ever forgotten it. No small part of any success I may have achieved is due to the habit I learned in early life, of being on time and persistently sticking to a task until it was completed.

Father, in his more quiet way, encouraged us also, and we were always sure that our parents were pleased with any success we might gain. Father was a great reader and always kept up with current events. For the time in which they lived, the members of his family were well-educated. Three of his sisters and two brothers were school teachers, and his oldest brother, Jasper, was a graduate of Allegheny College.

Living in a community with early-day manners, Father somehow kept himself aloof from the profanity and vulgarity of the time. Never, as a boy or man, did I ever hear my father use a profane or obscene expression. He used neither tobacco nor alcoholic liquor. His ideals were unusually high. His counsel and admonition were always safe to follow.

Father was the only man in our neighborhood who subscribed to a weekly newspaper. It was the *Toledo Blade,* then under the editorship of David R. Locke, author of the Petroleum V. Nasby papers. The family all read the *Blade.* During the summer of 1876, the Centennial Exposition, celebrating the century

22

of the signing of the Declaration of Independence, was held in Philadelphia. We eagerly awaited the coming of the *Blade* and read accounts of the exposition.

It was customary, after the preaching service on Sunday, for several of the older men to gather under the big beech tree in our front yard to spend the afternoon. One day Father happened to mention that he had read in the *Blade* that a man named Bell had displayed at the Exposition a contrivance called the telephone with which people half a mile apart might talk to each other.

The brethren under the beech tree didn't believe it. They wanted to hear the piece read. Father called to me, "Charley, go into the house and bring me the *Blade*." I did so, and Father read aloud the account, perhaps half a column in length, setting forth the bare outline of Alexander Graham Bell's great invention. This was all that was needed as a topic of discussion lasting the rest of the afternoon. It was argued pro and con; Father had to reread the article. The consensus was that there was some mistake, it just could not be true. The idea of the human voice being carried on a wire was preposterous. The men couldn't believe it, and they wouldn't believe it, and they didn't believe it.

After several hours' discussion, as the sun was going down behind the western hill, the party broke up, the men starting home to do the evening chores. Uncle Joe Morrison, the leader of the doubting Thomases, delivered the parting shot. As he started down the path toward his farm, he summed up the discussion as follows: "That paper is wrong, it must be a hollow tube and not a wire. Anybody with any sense at all knows that the human voice cannot travel over a wire. It's agin nature; and what's more, it's agin Scripture."

Once or twice a year the family drove sixteen miles to Marietta to attend the Washington County Fair or the Soldiers'

23

Reunion. It was our custom to get up at three o'clock in the morning, feed the horses, get breakfast, and be ready to start by four. The trip was made in the farm wagon, the only conveyance we possessed, the horses traveling in a walk. I still remember how Father would point out the constellations in the morning sky; Orion, which he called the Yard-L, and the Pleiades or Seven Sisters.

We would arrive at Marietta about eight o'clock, do some shopping, and attend the fair or the reunion. Late in the afternoon we would start home, arriving long after dark. The trip to Marietta was an important event in our lives, to which we looked forward, and which we afterward discussed for weeks.

One of the greatest surprises of my life occurred long afterward, when I revisited Ohio. With some boyhood friends, I started from Marietta in an automobile to visit the old home. During all these years, in the back of my mind I had remembered the four-hour trip. When we went over the same road in twenty minutes, it was unbelievable. But it was true.

I must have been about ten when I saw President Rutherford B. Hayes at the Soldiers' Reunion in Marietta. About all I can remember was the crowd, the parade headed by a brass band (the first one I had ever heard), then a carriage drawn by two white horses, and a man with long white whiskers standing and bowing to the cheering crowd.

For many years General Rufus Dawes, Sr., was our district congressman in southern Ohio. Before each election he would "stump his district," traveling with team and buggy, making speeches at the towns and country schoolhouses. The farmers would gather "at early candlelight" and listen to the great man expound the "pure and unadulterated" doctrine of Republicanism. How he would shake his long black whiskers as he lambasted the Copperheads and Democrats!

His son Charley Dawes used to make the trip with his father

24

to look after the team while the Congressman was shaking hands with his constituents. While the "Fathers in Israel" were inside the schoolhouse devoutly drinking in the pure doctrine, we boys would slip out on the playground and play games, blackman, hide-and-seek, and crack-the-whip. Even then, Charley Dawes always insisted on being the whip-cracker. I little thought that he would become vice president of the United States, cracking the whip over the Senate.

In 1886, the year I was eighteen, my parents mortgaged the farm and bought another team of horses, so that Father and I might engage in teaming in the oil fields near Macksburg and Elba. These oil fields had been opened up some months before, and there was great excitement in the community. The unusual price of four and five dollars per day was being offered for team work, two dollars per day being the regular price for man and team. We expected to make our fortunes in a few months, but about the time we were well established, development ceased in the oil fields, and we were thrown out of work. Father and I then went across the Ohio River into West Virginia and secured work hauling lumber and cross ties from mountain saw-mills to the railroad.

During the next winter our parents decided to sell the farm, leave Ohio, and move to Kansas. The twenty-acre farm was sold at a price of thirty-five dollars per acre, but after the mortgage was satisfied and some outstanding debts paid, little remained beyond the amount required to buy railroad tickets. On the trip west we rode in the day coach, sleeping as best we could.

CHAPTER 2

THE GOULDS MOVE TO KANSAS

THE SKY was a blue dome. The horizon was a circle
stretching away in all directions for unnumbered miles. There
was no timber; nothing to meet the eye but grass-covered plains.
Roads were little more than trails wandering across the open
prairie. Homes were chiefly dugouts, sod houses, and claim
shanties. This was western Kansas in the eighteen eighties.

What a contrast to the old home in Ohio with its timbered
hills, narrow valleys, swiftly flowing streams, little hillside fields,
and big farmhouses and barns! Ohio had had time to ripen.
Kansas was still raw.

We came to Kansas in April, 1887, and settled at the little
town of Ninnescah, afterwards called Cunningham, in western
Kingman County, about sixty miles west of Wichita. Taylor
Watkins and his brother Hamilton, with their families, former
neighbors of ours in Ohio, had come to Kansas several years
earlier. We had corresponded with them and they had advised
us to locate in Kingman County. Half a dozen other families
near by had come from our section of Ohio. They welcomed us
and did much to aid us in getting started in the new country.
Towns were few, so were schools and churches, but the people
were warm-hearted and hospitable, a happy, hopeful people,
eager to help the newcomers, and we soon felt ourselves among
friends.

During my pilgrimage nearly four score years on this mundane sphere, I have lived in many different surroundings and have mingled with many kinds of people. The happiest, jolliest, most hopeful people I have ever known anywhere have been the settlers in a new country. For where there is hope there is happiness, and these people had much for which to hope.

And today nothing irks me so much as to read one of the so-called modern realists, the professional folklorist, who, "with a plethora of zeal and a paucity of knowledge," attempts to describe something about which he knows nothing except what he has learned by reading some other realist's books. I am talking about the individual who uses much white paper to deplore the purely imaginary experiences of the early settlers. His books abound in such phrases as "dull, gray lives," "dreary, shabby surroundings," "hopeless, sodden monotony," "helpless struggles," "drab, uninteresting outlook," "poverty-ridden existence," and "desolate and forlorn viewpoint." These expressions, and others similar, run through his literary efforts like an ominous motif through a Wagnerian opera.

Please take it from one who knows, these were not an unhappy people, but joyous, singing, full of the zest of living. They were strong men and women, these early settlers on the plains, who looked the world in the face and took good and bad fortune in their stride. "The timid never started, the weaklings never arrived." These people need no sympathy. Rather should they have the envy and admiration of us all.

We came to Kingman County too late to "take up a claim." All the free land in the county, except a few scattered "forties," had been homesteaded several years before we arrived. A railroad had been built through the county from booming Wichita westward to Greensburg, and a few little towns had sprung up along this road, one of which was Ninnescah, our destination.

I was a strong, husky youth of nineteen, not afraid of work, and at once I began looking for a job. I soon found work with a nursery company that had the contract for planting several orchards around Kingman. For several weeks I worked at a salary of $1.25 per day, the highest wage I had ever received. My job was to dig holes and set out young apple and peach trees.

Father had rented an eighty-acre farm a mile east of Ninnescah. There was no house on the farm and we lived in a dugout, all underground. We went down six steps into the dugout. The floor was of dirt. It had a front room with a stove and table, and a back room with two beds. The few bits of furniture which we had brought from Ohio more than filled both rooms. A sod stable with a pole-and-prairie-grass roof sheltered the two horses, Jeff and Logan, Father had bought. After paying for the horses, a wagon, and the incidental expenses necessary to moving, we had less than fifty dollars left of the money from the sale of the Ohio farm.

Father borrowed farm tools from the neighbors and planted a corn crop on about forty acres; we also planted a garden, most of which failed to grow. I spent the rest of that summer doing odd jobs for farmers in the neighborhood, chiefly plowing and cultivating corn. Crops grew nicely during the spring and early summer months, but just as the corn was in tassel, the sky quit raining and the hot winds came. To one who has never experienced Kansas hot winds, the words will convey little meaning. Day after day of burning, blistering wind from the southwest; wind that scorched the skin like a blast from a furnace; hot wind that dried up the vegetation till the green leaves of the corn turned white, then rattled and blew away. This was our first experience with Kansas winds, but by no means the last. Father and Mother were almost heart-broken when they saw the result of the year's work disappear. There was not enough corn produced on the forty-acre field to keep one horse during the winter.

We discovered, one morning, a wounded pelican floundering about on the ground near the stables. Father thought that probably a flock of pelicans in flight had been fired upon by a hunter, and this bird had been so badly wounded he could go no farther. It was indeed unusual to see this species of water-fowl so far inland, and the pelican proved to be a real curiosity, both to the family and to the neighbors. His chief food was fish, which the children caught for him in near-by streams. The immense bill with the sac below held, when distended, a small pailful of water, and, while one of us held open the bill, another poured water and fish into the pouch-like throat. After a series of minor convulsions, the water was strained out and the fish were swallowed whole. It was always great fun to feed the pelican. After he had been our pet for two or three weeks, we discovered the bird was gone. His wounded leg had healed and we always suspected that he had heard from the air the call of other pelicans and had been able to rejoin his kind in their annual northern migration.

Meanwhile, we bargained for a two-room house in Ninnescah, and, in the early fall, we moved into town. Here I contracted typhoid fever and lay at the point of death for several weeks. Mother's good nursing, with the assistance of kind neighbors, finally brought me through, but my physical condition was such that I was able to do no work for several months. During the following spring, I attended school at Ninnescah.

I rented a few acres of garden and truck land and raised garden vegetables, which I marketed in the little town. It was my custom to rise at four o'clock, gather my radishes, beans, and cucumbers, haul them to Ninnescah on a buckboard, ped-dle them from door to door, and then go back to the garden and work the rest of the day at hoeing and weeding.

A tornado came along that spring and blew down several houses close to us. The family stood and watched the black, whirling, twisting, funnel-shaped cloud coming toward us from the southwest. When it struck the edge of town, half a mile away, the others retreated down cellar and begged me to come after them. I wanted to appear brave and stood at the window to watch boards, hay, and everything loose go whirling into the air. Once was enough.

That summer I decided to try teaching school. I had no education beyond that obtained in the country schools, equivalent, perhaps, to the eighth grade, but, on comparing myself with certain teachers whom I had met, I decided that I knew about as much as the average. In order to get a certificate to teach, it was necessary to attend the summer Normal Institute and take an examination. Three country boys, Seldon Webster, Mason Liebhart, and I, drove in a lumber wagon twenty miles to Kingman, rented a vacant house and "bached" while we attended the Normal. The greater part of our provisions came from the home farms. Father, Mother or someone from Webster's home would drive to town on Saturdays and bring us home-baked bread and other supplies, chiefly garden vegetables.

The Normal Institute lasted four weeks. Since this was my first year, I was in the lowest, or third, grade along with other country boys and girls. We reviewed the common branches, history, grammar, arithmetic, geography and reading. The conductor of the Normal was Ansel Gridley, superintendent of the Kingman city schools. Later he taught history at Southwestern College, Winfield, Kansas. He was one of the most kindly men I have ever known and always a true friend to me. Many a young fellow did Professor Gridley aid by encouragement and example.

At the close of the Institute all three of us boys took the examination. Liebhart and I passed and received certificates. I remember as well as though it were yesterday, when, two weeks after the close of the normal, I was working in the garden and a neighbor came by with a letter from the county super-intendent. I knew it contained either a certificate to teach or a notification of failure. My heart was in my mouth as I opened the letter, but found a certificate authorizing me to teach in the public schools of Kingman County for one year.

But my troubles were not over, for when I started out to find a school I learned that I was too late. All the schools in Kingman County had been taken for the winter. So I went to Pratt County and there secured a four-months school at thirty dollars per month. From the county superintendent, I obtained a tem-porary certificate which entitled me to teach until the October examination, which I passed with credit.

This first school, taught during the winter of 1888-89, was in Hardscrabble District, twelve miles southwest of Ninnescah. Mother drove me down the faint angling road across the prairie the first day, and came after me every two or three weeks so that I might spend Saturday and Sunday at home. I secured board for ten dollars per month with the clerk of the school board and slept on a bunk in the kitchen with one of the boys. The school was the ordinary country school of the time, with three or four big boys who tried to run out the new teacher, some big girls who giggled when spoken to, and several smaller children who studied a little when carefully watched.

I shall never forget the sensations of the first morning when I opened school and looked into the wide-eyed faces of thirty youngsters, mostly towheads, who ranged in age from five to twenty years. I suppose I must have taught a fairly good school, at least the board gave me a good letter of recommendation and invited me to come back for another year. I had no particular trouble except that one or two big boys became unruly and had to be disciplined, but after we had reached an understanding everything became quiet and serene.

I would come to the schoolhouse about eight o'clock in the

31

morning, cross the road to a cornfield and get a bundle of corn stalks to be used for kindling, and start a fire. Then I swept and dusted the schoolroom and was ready for the pupils when they began to come down the road at nine.

I enjoyed my first year's teaching. To me it has always been a pleasure and a delight to watch the unfolding of young minds. I suppose that, judged by modern educational methods, my efforts this first year were very crude, but the fact remains that we all had a good time, and the youngsters improved in their "readin', ritin' and 'rithmetic," with geography, grammar, and a bit of history thrown in for good measure.

During the winter we had the usual spelling schools, ciphering matches, and literary societies at Hardscrabble and the near-by schools. The district east of us was known as West Point, because it was a sort of military academy, that is to say, the patrons indulged in an old-fashioned "knock-down and drag-out" on every possible occasion. The schoolhouse north was known as Poverty Ridge, the one south as Happy Hollow, and the one west by the somewhat suggestive but strictly euphonious name of Hell's Half Acre.

The school at Hardscrabble lasted only four months, and in April I found myself out of a job. I learned that a school, at a little town, Penalosa, seven miles northeast of home, was without a teacher. I rode over, applied for the position, and was employed for two months at forty dollars per month. It seemed that the teacher who had been there the winter before was a young chap just out of high school who had lacked discipline. He did not teach out his full term, and I naturally began the school with some misgiving, but, after two weeks, the pupils and I became acquainted and I had no further trouble.

I had bought a little, one-eyed bay pony named Seven, that had all the vices of the ordinary mustang and few of the virtues except the ability to get over the road. I boarded at home, seven miles away across the prairie, and made the trip night and morning. After leaving home the pony would take a long lope and hardly break it all the way to Penalosa. The trip usually required an hour and a quarter.

The next summer I again attended the Normal Institute at Kingman, took the examination, and received a second-grade certificate which entitled me to teach for two years. The conductor of this county Normal Institute was L. C. Wooster, then the president of a small academy in eastern Kansas. His wide interests covered various fields of the natural sciences.

During assembly hour Professor Wooster gave the teachers a series of talks on various scientific subjects: zoology, astronomy, physics, chemistry, and geology. Very elementary they must have been, but to a Kansas country boy, they opened up a new world. I especially remember his description of the amoeba, illustrated by crayon drawings on the blackboard. It was the most fascinating thing I had ever heard, and I drank in every word.

During the last week of the term, Professor Wooster gave an evening lecture on the "Geological Story of Kansas." Some of the other fellows said they were not interested in learning about rocks, but I attended, all eyes and ears. I have already told of my experience at this lecture. It was more than five years from that time before I even made a start toward geology, but the idea was always in my mind that sometime, somehow, I must be a geologist.

Next month I attended the Institute at Pratt, where I received a second-grade certificate. About this time, prompted by a suggestion from Mother, I realized that if I were going to be a teacher, I wanted to be the best teacher in Kingman County, and I began to spend my leisure time reading and studying. I joined a county reading circle and began to make the acquaintance of good literature. That winter I again taught at Penalosa, receiving forty-five dollars a month, which that year was the highest salary paid any country teacher in the county. I bought another pony, named him Eight, and a buggy and made the trips with my team, Seven and Eight, to and from school, morning and evening. My sister Minnie Rose drove with me a good part of the year, and in the spring she took the county examination and graduated from the eighth grade of the public schools.

In the meantime, Father had bought an eighty-acre farm on the Ninnescah River, three miles east of town, paying for it with a mortgage on the farm and a promissory note. We built a half-dugout in which we lived for three years. This one was larger and more pretentious than the one in which we had lived the first summer after coming to Kansas, as it was built in the side of a bank, and had only three steps down from the surface of the ground. It had a board floor and two rooms with a window and a door in the front and a window in the rear. I can vouch from personal experience that a dugout is warm in winter and cool in summer. I can also testify that the dirt roof will not always turn water, for many a night, when the rain was pouring, Father and I worked for hours dipping water off the floor with a tin pan into a pail, and throwing it out the front door into the yard.

Those were the years when poor folks lived in dugouts, partly underground, while the aristocrats lived in sod houses above ground. In Kansas, as in all new countries, the first settlers built their homes of the best material nearest at hand. There was no timber in this part of Kansas, so log houses were impossible, nor was there any stone with which to build stone houses; so settlers did the next best thing, built their houses of sod.

A sod house was not hard to build. With a breaking plow, the homesteader turned over long strips of prairie sod. With a spade, these strips were cut into blocks and these blocks, approximately three by ten by sixteen inches in size, were hauled to the site of the house and the walls laid up like brick walls, but without mortar. The roof was usually of dirt, but if the settler had money enough to buy boards at the lumber yard, they were used. The floor was often of dirt.

For fuel we burned cornstalks and twisted hay, or sometimes prairie chips. There was no wood in the country, corn cobs were scarce, and we did not have money to buy coal. One winter, when shelled corn was selling at the railroad for nine cents a bushel, many farmers burned ears of corn for fuel, but my parents did not look with favor on burning corn, even when the crop was plentiful and prices low.

One of my evening chores was to cut up enough cornstalks to keep fire through the evening and get breakfast the next morning. With a long corn knife, I cut the stalks into stove lengths and carried them in an old wash boiler or a bushel basket to fill a box behind the kitchen stove. After supper, while three of the family were reading or sewing, one of us sat near and kept poking cornstalks into the old cook stove, which heated the dugout.

One kind of Kansas weather which we never learned to enjoy was the blizzards which occasionally, during the winter months, swept in from the north. Usually a blizzard was preceded by several mild, balmy days, "a weather breeder"; then, suddenly, far in the north, one might see a dark cloud spreading across the horizon and come rolling over and over. The wind, which had been in the south, changed abruptly to the north, the temperature suddenly fell, sometimes to zero; snow filled the air, and the blizzard was on. There was a scurrying about to see that stock was safe in good shelter, chickens were shut up, an adequate supply of fuel was brought into the house, for the blizzard sometimes lasted three or four days, with sleet, drifting snow, and biting wind.

One new experience was with prairie fires, which sometimes swept across the prairies carrying destruction with them. Fortunately, we suffered little damage, although on a few occasions, all the family had to run out in a hurry, and with wet gunny sacks, brooms, shovels or anything at hand, frantically beat out the flames to keep the fire from burning our pole-and-hay stable.

During the first year on this farm, Father broke out twenty acres of land with a sod plow and planted the land to corn. We set out an orchard and a grove of cottonwoods, which have since grown to be massive and sturdy trees.

It was during these years that I first became acquainted with the covered wagon. Our home was located on the old Cannon Ball trail, named for a stage driver "Cannon Ball" Green, who afterward founded Greensburg. This was the main east-west road from Wichita to southwestern Kansas. These were the days when western Kansas and southeastern Colorado were being settled. All day long the stream of covered wagons wound its way to the west, each wagon loaded with a family, the man, wife, and kids of assorted sizes, carrying all their worldly possessions. The travelers were accustomed to make overnight camp by the crossing of Ninnescah River on Father's farm, and we country boys would often wander down to sit around the campfire and hear them sing songs and tell stories. One of the most popular of these songs was "Uncle Sam's Farm," which I am giving at the close of this chapter. Another song which one heard, sometimes around the campfire, but perhaps more often on the way home from a party or a spelling school, was "The Little Old Sod Shanty on My Claim." It was a parody on "The Little Old Log Cabin in the Lane" and was sung to the tune of "Lily of the Valley." There were many verses.

"The Little Old Sod Shanty"

I am looking rather seedy now while holding down my claim,
And my victuals are not always of the best;

36

And the mice play shyly round me as I nestle down to rest,
In my little old sod shanty in the West.
Yet I rather like the novelty of living in this way,
Though my bill of fare is always rather tame,
But I'm happy as a clam on the land of Uncle Sam,
In the little old sod shanty on my claim.

REFRAIN:
The hinges are of leather and the windows have no glass,
While the board roof lets the howling blizzard in,
And I hear the hungry coyote as he slinks up through the
grass,
Round the little old sod shanty on my claim.

Another song, popular in those days, was sung to the tune of "Beulah Land" and the chorus ran something as follows:

Oh Kansas land, fair Kansas land,
As on my own rich farm I stand;
I look away across the plain
And see them come, great clouds of rain.
It makes our corn, it makes our hay,
For Kansas rains come any day.

A few years later, after "going west to grow up with the country," when western Kansas and Colorado were experiencing one of their periodic droughts, the boom broke, and the covered wagons, now more dilapidated, turned eastward and again streamed past our home. The settlers were going back to "live with the wife's folks."

Before we left Ohio some of the neighbors were solicitous, fearing that when we went West the Indians would get us. But

37

when we had arrived, we found that there were no more Indians in Kansas than there had been in Ohio. In fact, during the six years we lived in Kingman County, I do not remember having seen an Indian. There was a story current regarding an "Indian scare" that had occurred some years before, but it had proved to be a false alarm and nothing ever came of it.

This was the time when Oklahoma was first being opened to settlement. I did not "make the run." Why should I? Suppose I got a farm, what would I do with it? For even this early I had resolved that I did not intend to be a farmer all my life. I had had enough of the joys of farm life to last me indefinitely. At that time I was not at all sure just what my life work was to be—teaching perhaps, geology I hoped—but I knew it would not be following a team of horses up and down corn rows, taking time out night and morning to milk the cows and slop the hogs.

Several of the neighborhood boys, friends of mine, outfitted covered wagons and joined the mobs at the border, made the run and secured claims, some in Old Oklahoma, others, later, in the Cheyenne Country or in the Cherokee Outlet. But in spite of repeated invitations from the youngsters and admonitions by the elders, I remained at home, uninterested.

The Ninnescah River which ran through our farm is a spring-fed stream of pure water. The channel is filled with quicksand, and many homesteaders, fresh from some Eastern state, not understanding conditions, would drive into the river and stop to water their horses. The wheels of the wagon would begin to sink in the sand. Many times Father had to unhitch his team from the plow to pull someone out of the river.

In those days goose and duck shooting was good along the Ninnescah. Every spring and fall the wild fowl passing over would stop for several days along this stream. I have seen the river bottoms on Father's farm black with ducks and white with geese and brant. I had an old muzzle-loading musket, equally dangerous at both ends, and when the game lit on the sand bars, I would slip down to the river, crawl through the sandburs, fire into the bunch, and bring home half a dozen wild duck for dinner. As I now remember, fifteen ducks at one shot was my record. Bass were plentiful in some of the little streams and ponds, and part of my leisure time was spent in fishing.

But there was little time for recreation. When I was not teaching or studying, I was working on the farm or helping about the house. During the school year I used to plan, months ahead, for a Saturday in order to make a trip or do some special work. My days were occupied with teaching and my evenings with spelling schools, literary societies, reading circles and other activities connected with school work. Neither was Sunday a day of complete rest, for, regardless of the weather, all the family attended services, both morning and evening, at our church in town three miles away.

The next summer, I attended Normal Institute and received a first-grade certificate. During the remainder of the vacation I tried my hand as a book agent. At that time, the Farmers Alliance was being organized throughout the West. I became a member, learned the grips, signs and passwords, and then secured the agency for a book *The Voice of Labor*, which gave the history of the Alliance. I traveled in a buggy over a good part of Kingman County, and in six weeks had sold 250 books. Taking orders for the books was not difficult, but delivering and collecting the money for them was an entirely different matter. At the close of the season's work, I had twenty-five copies of the book on hand, which had been ordered, for which I had to pay.

The next winter I taught in the home district, Walnut Hill. I had a successful term and was able to be at home more than I had been for some time. Father's crops had been fairly good for two years and we were considering building a frame house, but this was never done. The next summer I spent in canvassing

39

for books and attending Normal Institute. Minnie Rose attended the Normal with me this summer, and at the close she took the examination and received a certificate. I taught that winter at Brownell school about four miles away, receiving an advance in salary. Minnie Rose taught her first school three miles from home. We both boarded at home and drove to and from school, morning and night.

During these years it had been gradually borne in upon me that I was not getting anywhere. While I enjoyed teaching, I did not expect to be a country school teacher all my days. Somehow and somewhere, I got a vision of something higher and better. Maybe my geological conversion was working; at any rate, I decided that I wanted to go to college. I talked the matter over with my parents and they encouraged me; Minnie Rose thought it was the only thing to do. But some of the neighbors were very much wrought up to think I would spend the time and the good money necessary to get any more "book learning." I remember one old farmer, a friend of the family, who was very solicitous. He had two husky sons whose ambitions never rose above the barnyard. One day he stopped me in the road and said:

"Charley, I hear you are talkin' about goin' off some'ers to school."

"That's right, Uncle George," I replied.

"I'm afeard you're makin' a big mistake, my boy," he said. "What good will your egication ever do you? Right now you're one of the best teachers in Kingman County, makin' top wages, and you kin make forty er fifty dollars a month as long as you want to teach school. Why spend your time and money in gettin' more book larnin'?"

This was the tenor of the objections raised by several of the good friends and neighbors. They simply could not see the sense of a young chap who was already a successful country school teacher spending his time and money going off to college to get more education.

When I began considering what school I should attend, it was not easy to make a choice. At that time, I do not believe that I had ever heard of a state university, and I certainly had never seen the outside of a college. During the summer months, a few teachers from Kingman County had gone to the State Normal School at Emporia. Others had attended a private school at Great Bend, and for some months I seriously considered going to this school.

About this time, our presiding elder, the Reverend J. D. Botkin, came to Cunningham to hold quarterly meeting. When our minister told him that Charley Gould was planning to go somewhere to school, the Reverend Botkin took half an hour to convince me that the only place for a good Methodist to attend school was the Methodist College at Winfield, Kansas. I had no particular choice in the matter, one school looked as good as another to me, and so I decided to go to Winfield. I have always been glad that the Reverend Botkin turned my feet toward a denominational college.

This is one of the songs that the homesteaders used to sing after supper when they were gathered by the light of the campfire at the crossing of the Ninnescah on Father's farm. I shall never forget one night when there were half a dozen wagons camped by the roadside. The melody was carried by a woman with a glorious soprano voice which rang out on the still night air, and all the crowd, men, women, and children joined in the chorus:

"UNCLE SAM'S FARM"

Of all the mighty nations in the east or in the west,
O, this glorious Yankee nation is the greatest and the best,

41

We have room for all creation and our banner is unfurl'd,
Here's a gen'ral invitation to the people of the world.

REFRAIN:
Then come along, come along, make no delay;
Come from ev'ry nation, come from ev'ry way,
Our lands, they are broad enough, don't be alarm'd
For Uncle Sam is rich enough to give us all a farm.

CHAPTER 3

A COUNTRY BOY
GOES TO COLLEGE

"BEAUTIFUL FOR SITUATION," wrote an enthusiastic Methodist minister, quoting from Psalms XLVIII, in describing Southwestern College. And to a country boy coming to college from the flat prairies of western Kansas the simile was apt. The gray stone building located on a hill east of Winfield, overlooking the beautiful valley of Walnut River, could be seen for miles. I have seen it a thousand times since but never without a thrill. To me it was, and still is, an inspiration, for it was here that I began to live. Here the eyes of my understanding were opened.

My entrance into college was by no means spectacular. I don't think anyone knew I had arrived on the campus. The president was M. E. Phillips and there were perhaps a dozen instructors.

I had the ordinary country boy's notions about college. I realized I was deficient in many branches and wanted to make up everything possible during the first year. There were not sufficient blank spaces on the front of my enrollment card to list all the various studies I wanted to take, so I turned the card over and wrote two studies on the back. I started with ten different classes, but by the time the term was half over, I had dropped half of them and was trying to keep from failing in the others. Geometry was almost too much for me, and beginning Latin was a headache.

During this first term in college, I did one thing for which I

43

have always been glad. I joined the best literary society in school, the "Athenian." Many young men who were members of this society have become noted. A speaker of the Kansas house of representatives, a professor at Yale University, a millionaire in Los Angeles, the pastors of three large churches in the East, and a number of successful businessmen have been members of this society.

The spring term was over in June, but I remained for a six-weeks summer term. During this time I first attended the Winfield Chautauqua Assembly. This was to me an eye-opener and a soul-awakener. The popular lectures and concerts given twice a day and the various classes and round tables which I attended gave me an insight into a new world. I was hungry for these things and enjoyed them to the full. If I were asked to name in order of importance the three things which most profoundly influenced me during my first year at college, I should say "The Athenian Literary Society, the Chautauqua Assembly, and the classroom work."

At the close of the summer term I returned home, and next winter taught at a country school. During this winter, it was decided it would be best to sell the farm for what we could get, crops having been poor, and move to Winfield, so that both my sister and I could attend college and live at home. Minnie Rose had been teaching for two years and had made a success as a primary teacher. My parents sold the Kingman County farm and we moved to Winfield, where we rented a house and I again entered college. I attended the latter part of the spring term and also the summer term. The entire family enjoyed the Chautauqua Assembly. Sometime later Mother took up the work of the Chautauqua Literary and Scientific Circle, which she studied for four years. When she was sixty-four years of age, Mother graduated from this course and received her diploma, which was thereafter one of her most prized possessions.

44

The next fall both Minnie Rose and I began the year in college. But funds soon ran low. We were disappointed by not getting some money we had expected to secure from the sale of the farm, and after a few weeks in school I found that I must teach again. During this winter, 1893–94, I served as principal of schools at Ashland, Kansas. There were two other teachers, in the primary and intermediate grades, while I carried all the eighth grade and such work as was offered in high school branches. I taught physics during the noon hour, general history at afternoon recess, and three of the big boys came in the evening twice a week for chemistry.

It was during this winter that I got my first real inkling of geology, the science to which I have since devoted my life. One Saturday, in company with several of the big boys, I had gone on a picnic into the hills north of Ashland. There are several distinct geological formations in that country, the red beds being found along the valleys, with a black shale of Cretaceous age on the slopes, while the hills and uplands are covered with white Tertiary shales. This Cretaceous black shale contains many fossils, particularly oyster shells as big as one's hand, and bones of prehistoric reptiles. On this trip I found a number of fossil shells, and also two femurs of some animal. I showed them to a doctor in Ashland who decided that they were not human bones, but he did not know what they might be.

The finding of these fossils revived my desire to learn something about geology. I sent away for a textbook on the subject, LeConte's *Elements of Geology*. This I found so interesting that I read and reread the different chapters until I knew many of them almost by heart. In the meantime I had learned that Kansas had a state university, and reasoned that there must be a museum at that place, although I had never seen a museum.

I sent the bones to the president of the state university at Lawrence. He turned them over to S. W. Williston, professor

45

of geology and paleontology. Professor Williston wrote me a very cordial letter saying that the bones were those of a prehistoric reptile *Plesiosaurus,* and advised me to look for others. From that time on, I spent every Saturday, and some Sundays also, in the hills hunting bones and combing over every outcrop of black shale for twenty miles north and northwest of Ashland.

Finally one afternoon, I found what I had been looking for. Exposed on a shale bank, lay a row of vertebrae as large as the backbone of a horse, with a few leg bones and fragments of the skull. Almost a complete skeleton, not very well preserved, but sufficient for identification.

I shall never forget the peculiar thrill that came to me as I stood looking at those fossils. Having in mind the lessons from LeConte, I could interpret what I saw. For untold millions of years those bones had been embedded in the shale. They had lain there ever since that long-gone prehistoric time when an ancient sea lizard, the *Plesiosaur,* having lived out his life, had sunk to the bottom of the Cretaceous sea and had been buried in the mud and ooze. Ages, eons, passed; the sea was drained away. The mud and ooze slowly changed to black shale and the country became dry land. Continents arose, then erosion started to plane down the land areas.

Then, during later geologic time, there was another period, the Tertiary, when terrific floods swept down from the Rocky Mountains and buried the whole country under great loads of sand and clay debris.

Again erosion began its work. Valleys were carved out and the rocks laid bare, until finally, after uncounted ages, the particular little canyon in which I was working had been eroded out. The bones of the *Plesiosaur,* buried since Cretaceous times, were finally uncovered and lay revealed on the black shale, and I, Charley Gould, a Kansas school teacher, had the great good fortune to find them.

46

When I was a young man some of the brethren in our church believed in a "second blessing." If I can date my geological conversion to the time when, on a hot August night in the little school house in Kingman, Professor Wooster held up before a group of country school teachers two slabs of red sandstone containing ripple marks and mud cracks, just so definitely can I date the time and the place when, all alone on a shale bank in a canyon in Clark County, Kansas, I found the petrified skeleton of the prehistoric monster *Plesiosaurus*. Again I felt the spinal shiver. This was my second blessing.

Need there be surprise when the geologist stands in wonder before his discoveries in the rocks, awed by his own insignificance!

I dug out these bones and packed and shipped them to Professor Williston. He identified the bones as belonging to a new species of fossil reptile which he did me the honor to name *Plesiosaurus gouldii*. This was the first of my scientific progeny, and I am sure no little boy with his first red-top boots was ever prouder than I was.

At the close of the school term at Ashland, Professor Williston came to Clark County, and I spent several delightful days with him collecting fossils. We secured a horse and a two-wheeled cart and lived off the ranchmen while we visited practically every locality from which I had collected fossil bones and shells.

I owe much to Professor Williston. During the various talks we had while out in the hills together, I told him something of my hopes and aspirations and that I was seriously considering becoming a geologist. He endeavored to dissuade me. Among other things he said: "It's a dog's life, Gould, and there is nothing in it. A geologist never makes any money, he works hard all his days, he is called a fool and a crank by nine-tenths of the people he meets, and he lives and usually dies unappreciated. I would advise you to try something easy, like law or

47

medicine or selling shoes, or stick to school teaching. There is more eating in those jobs than there is in geology."

But after I had convinced him that it was geology or nothing for me, he began to give me oceans of good advice. Among other things, he said:

"Whatever you do or do not do, Gould, begin early to publish. I have watched scientists for twenty years, and it is my experience that it is the scientific damnation of any young person starting out in a scientific career to go five years without publishing. The world does not know, nor does it care that you are alive, and the world is not going to give you the glad hand. It is up to you to take the world by the throat and make it recognize you."

I, being diffident, said: "But what shall I publish?"

"That does not matter," Professor Williston replied. "The essential thing is to break into print, get your thoughts into type, get them on paper. Write about these bones we have been collecting, or go out in the Flint Hills east of Winfield, your home, make some cross sections of the rocks, collect some fossils, write a paper, and get it published. It does not make so much difference what you print, as long as you get into type."

This admonition I consider to be one of the most valuable things that ever entered into my scientific experience. My friends have sometimes accused me of publishing too much. My bibliography now includes about three hundred titles. But I wish to bear testimony to the correctness of Williston's views. It has been my experience, as it was his, that the young person who starts out in a scientific career and does not publish never gets his head above the surface. He may be ever so able a scientist, but the world never knows it.

Let me pause here and devote a paragraph to Samuel Wendell Williston, one of the truly great men of my acquaintance and one who very profoundly influenced my life. He was a teacher of teachers, a trainer of scientists. He drew young men to him and instilled into them the desire to go forward to better things. They fed on his enthusiasm, were warmed by his inner fires. Today I can count a score of scientists scattered across the continent who received their inspiration from Professor Williston. He was a tireless worker. His chief specialty was vertebrate paleontology, and for many years his collections of Cretaceous and Permian reptiles at the museums of the University of Kansas and the University of Chicago were unexcelled. He was also the best American authority on *Diptera* (flies).

At the end of the trip with Professor Williston, I came back to Winfield and enrolled in college for a part of the spring term, and later in the summer the Gould family again attended the Chautauqua. In August of that year, I made a trip with Robert T. Hill, of the United States Geological Survey, into southwestern Kansas, to examine some deposits along Medicine River. Near the head of this stream there are excellent exposures of shales and sandstones of Cretaceous age like those in Clark County. F. W. Cragin, of Washburn College at Topeka, had visited this region and published an article on the geology of the country. Hill and Cragin were scientific rivals and Hill's object in visiting the locality on Medicine River was to review Cragin's work.

Hill joined me at Winfield and we proceeded to Medicine Lodge. There we secured an outfit consisting of team, covered wagon, driver, and saddle horses, drove up the Medicine and camped for several days at the Black Hills west of Sun City, and afterwards at Belvidere. Hill made a number of geological sections and collected extensively from the various formations. After he left Belvidere for field work in Texas, I remained for a week, collecting from different geological horizons. I secured twenty boxes of fossil shells and rock specimens which I sent to Washington. In a paper which Hill wrote describing the area

49

visited, he mentioned that he had met a "promising young geologist named Gould." This was the first time my name got into scientific literature.

And as with Williston, so with Robert T. Hill. He was one of the greatest reconnaissance geologists America has ever seen. A geological genius, who seemed to know intuitively just where a certain formation should outcrop. A man who could travel over the country, make a few notes here, measure a section there, make a sketch yonder, climb a hill farther on to take a "look see," and come back to the office to write a report which would be more nearly correct than one made by the ordinary geologist who had spent a season in the field. Hill had been a Texas cowboy in Comanche County and had driven herds of cattle north across the plains to Kansas. A graduate of Cornell, professor of geology at the University of Texas, member of the U.S. Geological Survey, and the originator of the term Comanche, as applied to a series of formations, he was a great man and a thorough scientist.

This brief association in 1894 was the beginning of a friendship that lasted until his death in 1941. Many were our contacts during those forty-seven years, in his office, in my office, in the field, in different states all the way from Missouri to California, in his home, and in my home. We had many things in common.

I felt highly honored when I was invited to form one of a small group of geologists and friends who met at Comanche, Texas, where on Round Mountain we scattered to the winds the ashes of this great man. It was on Round Mountain seven miles west of Comanche that, in 1874, the orphan boy, Bobby Hill, first picked up fossil shells.

I was indeed fortunate that I early met the two masters, Williston and Hill, sat at their feet, and from them learned something of how to read the story of the rocks.

The contacts made in the spring and summer of 1894 defi-

50

nitely fixed the current of my life. I was then twenty-six years old and only fairly started in my college work. From that time on there never was a shadow of a doubt as to what my life's work should be. I knew I must be a geologist, and could never be anything else. On my return home from the trip with Hill, when I told my parents of my decision to become a geologist, they were disappointed. I have sometimes thought that they had set their aspirations on their boy becoming a Methodist preacher. But they soon became reconciled to my views, and afterwards did everything in their power to aid me in completing school and fitting myself for my life work.

During the next winter, funds were again low and I was obliged to teach. I learned that the school at Maple City was without a principal. I drove across the rocky hills, and after some difficulty got the members of the school board together. One of them I found hauling pumpkins, another I chased up an apple tree, while the third had gone to Arkansas City and did not return until ten o'clock that night. But I succeeded in getting a meeting of the board, and was employed for the year at fifty dollars a month.

On my way to and from Maple City, I often went by way of Dexter. It was here that I located my first anticline. Some years later, several wells were drilled for oil on this anticline, and gas was encountered. But the gas would not burn. The people called it "no-good gas," and it was turned loose and permitted to escape into the air.

Professor Cady of the department of chemistry at the University of Kansas was compiling analyses of natural gas from Kansas wells. He obtained a sample from one of the Dexter wells and on examination found it contained a larger helium content than any other known gas. But the damage had already been done. Hundreds of millions of cubic feet of gas containing helium, now so useful in industry, had been permitted to escape

51

and was lost to the world, the result of man's criminal ignorance.

One advantage at Maple City was the fact that there was good geology near by, and I spent many of my evenings and Saturdays in the field, studying the various formations and collecting fossils. I made a number of trips into the Osage and Kaw nations, which lay to the south, in Indian Territory, or what is now Oklahoma.

One day while traveling across the prairie in the northern part of the Kaw Reservation, I found a set of wagon irons, almost complete. There were three rusted tires lying close together, and a fourth about fifty yards away, also the irons of the hubs, hounds, standards, tongue, and other parts of the wagon, scattered over half an acre of ground. Near by were some bones and a skull, which I recognized as parts of the skeleton of a horse. In those days bones were so common on the prairie that I thought nothing further about them, but the wagon irons piqued my curiosity.

Some weeks later, I was riding in company with a man who had been in that country almost from the time of the first settlement. We passed near where the bones and wagon irons were strewn about and this is the story he told me:

One summer soon after the Kaw Indians had moved to their reservation in northern Oklahoma, they leased their grass to some Texas cattlemen. These men brought a trainload of Chihuahua steers from Old Mexico and turned them loose on the range. Long-horned, dun-colored, savage brutes, wild as deer, these cattle had scarcely seen a man, a dog, or a wagon. Indeed, it was hardly safe for a man on horseback to ride among them.

A few days after the cattle had been turned into the Kaw pasture, Bill Ferguson, a settler near the Oklahoma line started down into the Kaw Reservation for a load of wood. His dog was with him. He didn't come back.

Next day, becoming alarmed, the neighbors started down to

hunt for him, and all they found was a trampled mass of flesh and bones, nothing that looked like horses or man or dog, with broken pieces of a wagon scattered around on the trampled prairie. As the party approached, two coyotes slunk off into the brush. The neighbors gathered up what they could recognize of the man and took the remains home for burial.

What had happened was probably this. The half-wild cattle had seen the dog and begun to follow it. Becoming frightened, the dog had run under the wagon, and the cattle in their savage rage had gored and trampled the horses, man, and dog to death, and even demolished the wagon and scattered the broken pieces over the prairie.

The next year a prairie fire came along and burned up the wooden parts of the wagon. Many years later the iron and the bones were still lying where the cattle had left them.

There were several advanced students in the school at Maple City, and I organized classes in beginning Latin, general history, civics, algebra, and American literature, some of which I taught after school and some during the noon hour. I was glad to do this extra work, not only in order to help the ambitious young people, but also because it gave me a chance to brush up my meager knowledge of these subjects. I learned more Latin teaching my beginning class than I ever did in the classroom.

My whole college career was a hand-to-mouth experience. Of all the years from 1892 to 1899 that I attended school, there was only one year when both my sister and I were in college together. Either she or I taught school to help pay the expenses of the family. During these years Mother was keeping boarders, while Father did odd jobs about the town, and during the summer raised what garden vegetables and small crops he could. All the Gould family worked together with the one object of putting Minnie Rose and Charley through college.

The next summer I was very anxious to do field work, for I

realized that, if I expected to become a geologist, I must study rocks at first hand. I had no money to pay expenses. So after canvassing the situation, I hit upon the plan of collecting fossils near Belvidere and Ashland and selling them. I wrote a number of letters to various universities and museums, both in the United States and in Europe, setting forth the fact that I expected to make a collecting trip into southwestern Kansas, and stating the character of fossils that I would probably secure. I suggested that the recipient invest ten, twenty, or fifty dollars in the trip, and offered to send a pro rata share of the specimens obtained. Some half a dozen men replied and contributed towards the expedition. Among others were W. B. Clark of Johns Hopkins University and E. H. Barbour of the University of Nebraska. These men sent sums varying from ten to fifty dollars, and I collected in all about $120 for the summer's trip.

Mother, who enjoyed camping almost as much as I did, accompanied me on this trip. The equipment consisted of a spring wagon with bows and cover, two ponies, a tent, and a light cooking outfit. There were also two boxes filled with old newspapers for wrapping fossils. Soon after commencement, we left Winfield and traveled westward through Wellington, Harper, and Medicine Lodge, up Medicine River to Belvidere, where we camped for nearly a month under a spreading elm tree near the town.

Belvidere is a collector's paradise, and I truly enjoyed the opportunity of gathering specimens. It was not work, it was play. To me there has always been something fascinating in finding a beautiful shell or bone which has been lying undisturbed for unknown millions of years, waiting for me to come along and pick it up. I secured some one hundred boxes of fossil shells, bones, and leaves, which I divided pro rata among those who had contributed towards the expenses of the expedition, and shipped them by freight from the little station. Later

54

Mother and I went west to the hills north of Ashland, where I had found my first fossils the year before, and collected from that region.

It was while we were camped at Belvidere that I learned from the local doctor the story of the two college professors who made the race for meteorites. In the late eighties, when the early settlers came to Kiowa County, they found, scattered around on the prairie near the head of Medicine River, a number of fragments of a peculiar black rock. Some pieces were as large as a gallon measure, most of them smaller. They occurred over several square miles of land and represented the fragments of a meteor that had burst and showered upon the earth's surface.

The settlers had no idea of their origin, and rock of any kind being scarce on the flat prairie, they were used for many purposes; weights for covers on milk crocks, door stops, weights on haystacks, and as foundations under claim shanties.

Now meteorites are of extreme scientific interest, chiefly because they are the only objects that are known to come to us from off the earth. Because of their scarcity, museums are always willing to pay a fair price for good specimens. While on a professional visit, my doctor friend at Belvidere, who had been a student at Harvard Medical School and had been through the Harvard museums, happened to see these rocks and thought they might be meteorites. So he wrote two letters describing them, one to President F. H. Snow of the University of Kansas, the other to Professor F. W. Cragin at Washburn College, Topeka, who had collected fossils at Belvidere.

These men got the letters the same day and both took the same westbound Santa Fe train for Belvidere. Each man was surprised to see the other on the train, for both had hoped that he alone knew of the meteorites. They sat together discussing the weather and various scientific problems, in fact everything except the one thing that was uppermost in the mind of each—meteorites.

At Newton, both men got off the train and bought tickets south on the Oklahoma branch. Again they occupied the same seat and discussed erudite problems. Both got off at Mulvane and bought tickets for Belvidere. When the train started west, both men were on board. Again they sat together but the conversation lagged. They were not only talked out, but the suspicion in the mind of each approached a certainty. Finally Snow could stand it no longer and asked Cragin point blank what his destination was. "The same as yours," said Cragin, "Belvidere. I'm after the same meteorites that you are trying to get."

So on the theory, "If you can't lick 'em, jine 'em," they agreed to work together and divide the spoils.

On arriving at Belvidere, they were met by the doctor, who drove them to the neighborhood where the meteorites occurred. They remained several days, collected all the fragments they could find, several hundred pounds in all, paying the settlers a very nominal price for them. Then, before leaving, they divided the various specimens as nearly equally as possible.

Professor Snow placed the greater part of his specimens in the museum of the University of Kansas, where many of them may be seen today. Professor Cragin sold many of his specimens to museums in eastern universities and in Europe.

And thereby hangs a tale. The president and trustees of Washburn College insisted that Cragin was an employee of the college, and therefore the specimens were the property of the school. But Cragin pointed out that he had paid his own expenses on the trip and by right of discovery was the owner of the meteorites. So Cragin sold the meteorites for several thousand dollars, but it cost him his job at Washburn.

Mother and I returned home early in September and the family moved to Maple City. I taught a second winter as principal, and Minnie Rose had the primary room. I took every opportunity to get into the field.

It was during this winter that I wrote my first geological article. Acting on Professor Williston's advice, I had gone over into the Flint Hills east of Winfield and prepared a geological cross section of the rocks. I sent the section with brief notes on the subject to Professor Haworth of the University of Kansas, who was preparing to publish a report on the Carboniferous rocks of the state. He included this section in his report. It is entitled "A Geologic Cross Section Across the Flint Hills of Kansas From Cedarvale to Winfield," and may be found on pages 30 to 34 of Volume 1 of the University Geological Survey of Kansas.

During the summer of 1896, I had my first season's field work in a well-organized geological party. Professor Haworth was sending into the field a number of men in order to secure data for a geological report which he was preparing. I wrote him asking if he had anything for me to do, and he replied, offering to include me in one of his field parties and to pay my expenses if I would donate my time. Notwithstanding the fact that I did not have money enough in sight to keep me in college during the next winter, this arrangement appealed to me. Professor Charles S. Prosser, who had taught geology at Washburn and had studied and published a number of articles on the Upper Carboniferous formations of Kansas, had charge of a party, which was to work throughout the central and southwestern parts of the state. I did not wish to miss the opportunity of a summer's work with him.

Acting on Professor Haworth's suggestion, I secured at Winfield, a team, covered wagon, tent, and one additional saddle horse. The instructions were to get everything as economically as possible because funds were limited. I assembled my outfit, tied the saddle horse behind the wagon, and started from Winfield to Newton, where I was to meet the third member of our party, J. W. Beede, whom I had never seen. At Newton I found a letter from Haworth instructing me to go to a lawyer's office at a certain hour. There I found a young fellow waiting for me. From that time until his death a few years ago, J. W. Beede and I were the warmest of friends, both scientific and personal.

Professor Haworth dropped into Newton the next day, looked us over, and decided that we might do. He sent us north to Salina, where we met Professor Prosser and started out on the summer's work. We spent nearly two weeks studying the various formations, particularly the Dakota sandstone, which caps the hills near Salina, then came south to Winfield, tracing out certain ledges of limestone along Walnut River. We then went west past Wellington, through Harper and Medicine Lodge, collected along Medicine River near Belvidere, then still farther west as far as Bear Creek in Clark County. At this point, Prosser and Beede left me alone to complete the work. Soon afterward, I received instructions that the funds were exhausted and to break camp and return.

This summer's work was of considerable benefit to me. The training with an eminent scientist like Prosser taught me many things. I served as cook for the outfit while Beede usually acted as teamster. The work was hard, but I enjoyed every minute of the time, and I consider it one of the most profitable seasons I ever spent in the field.

As young men have always done, especially throughout the West, on this trip we three chaps picked out nicknames for each other. Prosser became Cottonwood Charley, Beede was Dusty Roads, and I was dubbed Alkali Ike. Among ourselves those names were to last as long as the other two men lived.

Prosser suffered a tragic death at Columbus, Ohio, where he had served for many years as the head of the department of geology at Ohio State University. Beede taught geology for nearly two decades at the University of Indiana and became one of the outstanding authorities on the North American Permian. He died in 1940.

J. W. Beede was one of the finest characters I have ever known. Quiet, unassuming, sweet spirited, lovable, he came more nearly being a geological chum than any geologist of my acquaintance. Thrown together in early manhood, for more than forty years we saw eye to eye on matters geological. Trained under the same teachers, Prosser, Haworth, and Williston, interested in the same problems, often working in the same territory, wearing out sole leather on the same rocks, we came down the years mutually respecting each other and each other's opinions. No other man can ever take the place of my chum Beede.

After Prosser's death, Beede and I adopted another geologist who spoke our language, W. E. Wrather of Dallas, now director of the United States Geological Survey, as the third member of the trio, and on him we bestowed the cognomen Comanche Bill. Since Beede's passing, Wrather and I have not been able to agree on a man to take his place. There seems to be no other man.

The following winter, 1896–97, I attended college practically all the year. During this time Minnie Rose taught the primary grade at Caldwell, sending home money each month to help out with the expenses of the family. I was getting in closer touch with things and had become a leader in the Athenian Literary Society.

I was asked to become business manager of the college paper, and in this way I helped pay expenses. The faculty asked my good friend and teacher, Professor L. T. Weeks, head of the English department, to assume the editorship of the newspaper. I was very much surprised when he stopped me in the hall and asked me if I would accept the position of business manager.

He guaranteed me twenty dollars monthly for the work and a certain percentage of what I could make over that amount. To me, the experience was new but valuable. The revenue of the paper was derived partly from student subscriptions, which were seldom paid, and partly from advertising. I visited the businessmen in Winfield in endeavoring to secure ads for the paper. The first month or two I had much difficulty, but after a few issues, I found things coming my way, and I really enjoyed the work.

I was very fortunate in having the opportunity to spend the next field season in company with one of the greatest men whom America has ever produced, Lester F. Ward of Washington, D. C. He had achieved world-wide reputation in two very different sciences, sociology and phytopaleontology, or the study of fossil plants. While a clerk in the Treasury Department at Washington, he became acquainted with Major J. W. Powell, director of the U. S. Geological Survey. Ward took up the study of botany and made exhaustive collections of the plants along the Potomac River near Washington. In the course of his explorations, he found a certain formation of Lower Cretaceous age which contained many fossil plants. His interest soon became centered on these plants. At that time, there were only one or two men in America, and not to exceed a dozen in the world, who made any pretense of knowing anything about the study of plant paleontology.

After Mr. Ward had been studying plants for a few years, Major Powell offered him the position of plant paleontologist in the U. S. Geological Survey. He accepted the offer and for many years thereafter was the leading authority in North America on fossil plants.

For many years Ward had gone into the field every summer in order to collect fossil plants. He had named and described practically all the different species found on the Atlantic Coastal

Plain and had also collected extensively in Utah, Montana, Washington, and other northwestern states, but had not done any collecting in the Southwest.

I learned of Ward's name as being connected with plant paleontology and wrote him asking if he would care for some collections of fossil leaves which I might make at Belvidere. I had collected a number of leaf specimens and knew where many fossil leaves might be secured. To my surprise, I received a most cordial letter from him telling me that he had planned to spend the summer in southwestern Kansas, and asking me to become a member of his party. I was eager for the chance, particularly in view of the fact that he offered me seventy-five dollars per month and my expenses. I wrote him that I should be glad to go with him and asked for suggestions. He outlined his plans as to the outfit and instructed me as to when and where to meet him. I was on hand at the appointed time with the covered wagon and other camp equipment, and met a tall, spare, dignified man about fifty-five years of age, with a well-knit frame, Roman nose, face smooth-shaven, except for side whiskers, and kindly gray eyes. So I remember him as he stepped from the train to the depot platform at the little town of Belvidere. He loaded his well-worn traveling bag and roll of blankets into the back of the covered wagon, climbed up on the driver's seat beside me, and we started up Medicine River toward the collecting ground.

We made early camp near a spring in the shadow of a great ledge of sandstone. He helped me pitch tent; then, as a matter of camp courtesy to the guest, I asked him to choose the corner of the tent which he wished for his bed. But no tent for him. He preferred to sleep under the stars. Shouldering his bed roll, he carried it to a near-by patch of bluestem grass, where he tramped out a nest for his bed and spread his blankets, weighting down the four corners with stones to keep the wind from

61

disarranging them. In the meantime I had been busy building a fire, watering the horses, and staking them out to grass for the night. I heated water, made tea, opened canned goods, cut bread, fried bacon, and by the time he had washed the dust of travel from his face and hands, we were ready for the evening meal.

We would rise with the sun, eat breakfast, and start out, either on foot or on horseback, for the various collecting points within a few miles of Belvidere. Some days we would return laden with rocks containing delicate tracings of leaves, relics of by-gone ages; sometimes we would find nothing. During the summer we collected about forty boxes of extremely fine and rare specimens.

Many of the leaves were of the same type as those living at the present time in North America. We found leaves of such trees as oak, willow, sassafras, *Platanus* (sycamore), dogwood, and *Populus* (cottonwood). Along with them we found leaves of the fig, magnolia, a *Sequoia* (the big tree of California), eucalyptus, now native to Australia, and others which do not now grow in this country.

He explained to me that the ledge of sandstone in which the leaves occurred, found in the valley of Medicine River, represented an ancient sandy sea beach. In those far off, prehistoric times, the Lower Cretaceous, long, long before man appeared on earth, all of western Kansas had been an ocean. Along the shore grew trees, just as trees grow near the seacoast today. The leaves from these trees were blown off by the wind, or when frost came they fell to the ground, just as leaves do now. Many of these leaves fell into the soft mud and their prints were registered, just as we may sometimes find leaf prints in soft ooze along streams today. Other sand and mud was washed in by the tides or from the streams, the leaves were covered, and the impressions were preserved.

After a long time, so he said, the sea retreated and all this mud and sand slowly turned to rock. A continent arose where once all was ocean. Erosion had been at work during the millions of years since that time, and the leaf prints are again exposed. And here were we, two human beings, a Kansas school boy and a government scientist from Washington, with hammers, breaking away the rock and revealing what had been buried and preserved eons before.

To me it was all very wonderful. So simply, yet so convincingly, was the story unfolded, a bit at a time, that one could not disbelieve.

The conversations with Ward opened up new worlds to me. I had had very little opportunity of associating with men of broad achievements, certainly with none like him. When he found that I was receptive, and that I appreciated his instruction, he would spend hours in describing to me the relation and meaning of the various phenomena which we encountered. I remember learning the life history of two genera of trees still living in North America. These genera were the *Platanus* (sycamore) and the *Quercus* (oak). We found many *Platanus* leaves in these rocks and to me they looked as if they belonged to different species. He assured me that this was the fact. During Cretaceous times, the *Platanus* was one of the most common and diversified of the trees. There were in all perhaps thirty or forty different species living in North America, and their leaves had been described by paleontologists. Today there were but two species known in the world: the *Platanus occidentalis* found in America and the *Platanus orientalis* which occurs in the Old World. He explained to me, as I already knew, that today the sycamore is not a hardy tree, that while it grows to a large size, it is found chiefly along water courses; that the tree rots easily, is not good for lumber, and in fact is the last vanishing and decadent member of a long and worthy line of ancestors.

63

Very different was the *Quercus* or oak. During Cretaceous times there were few species of oak trees. The leaves were small and quite different in form and outline from the broad leaves of this tree today. The oak, however, has been developing and increasing since Cretaceous time, until today there are in America nearly fifty species of oak. The oak is one of our most thrifty hardwoods, and is unequaled for lumber and for firewood. *Quercus* is still developing, while *Platanus* is nearly extinct.

As the days passed, and as we collected hundreds of beautiful specimens of well-preserved leaves, I began to appreciate my new-found friend more and more. A wise man, a great man, one of America's leading authorities in two very abstruse sciences, a writer of learned books, a lecturer to learned societies, a teacher in great universities, the companion of the great and wise men of the earth, an adviser to presidents and cabinet members, he was withal as simple as a child. I have seen him sit by the hour and listen while farmers, ranchmen, and day laborers were engaged in talking over trivial matters, or trying to settle the destinies of mankind. They never suspected that the quiet, unassuming gentleman, sitting in their midst, was a man consulted by statesmen and the great men of the world, and one whose word was authority wherever it was heard.

He was never too busy to answer my questions, or to be interested in whatever rock, specimen, or flower I brought him. Not a stray dog wandered into camp but he would make friends with it; not a pony with a sore shoulder, but he would apply healing medicines. Even the meadow larks and doves about camp seemed to let him approach nearer than most of us, before taking flight. He found a nest of baby jack rabbits a hundred yards from camp and visited the little things night and morning, watching them grow, till they would hop to meet him when he approached and nibble dainties from his hand. Who could help loving and respecting a man like that?

64

And the talks we had around the campfire, I shall never forget them.

One night after a hard day's work, I had written my notes, crawled under my blankets and was dropping off to sleep when, from his bed in the bluestem grass, I heard that strong resonant voice start reciting the lines of Charlotte Perkins Gilman's poem, "Similar Cases," beginning "There was a little animal no bigger than a fox and on five toes he scampered over Tertiary rocks. They called him Eohippus, etc." The second part described "The anthropoidal ape, far smarter than the rest," and the third part "The neolithic man, an enterprising wight."

After I began teaching at the University of Oklahoma, I secured the entire poem, had it copied and distributed to my class in historical geology.

Several men have very profoundly influenced my life, my father, one of my early pastors, an old college teacher, the president of the institution under whom I did my early university teaching, Samuel W. Williston, Robert T. Hill, but more than all others, Lester F. Ward, the lovable, simple, wise man, scholar and scientist, whom I learned to love in camp in western Kansas so many years ago.

The following winter I spent in college. It really was my time to teach and let Minnie Rose go to school. I told her that if she would teach one more year and let me attend college, I would see to it that she might go to college the rest of her life, if she wished. To this she agreed, sending home a good part of her salary each month.

The next summer was again spent in southwestern Kansas and in the same region in which I had collected for the past four summers. By this time I had begun to know the geology of the region fairly well. I was again fortunate in being employed by Ward for the summer's field work. This year we were accompanied by T. W. Stanton, of the U. S. Geological Survey, who was recognized as the best authority in America on the invertebrate fossils of the Cretaceous.

I was instructed to secure an outfit at Winfield, where Ward was to meet me. I employed my old friend, J. E. Broadie, who furnished a covered wagon, team, and three saddle horses. As cook, I hired my schoolmate, Mark White. We assembled the outfit at Winfield and purchased supplies. Ward came directly from Washington and with him we started west toward Medicine River. At Belvidere Stanton joined the party, and we had a most profitable and enjoyable trip during the remainder of the summer. After having collected fossil shells and leaves at Belvidere, we worked westward into the locality which I had so often visited northwest of Ashland. From here we passed north across the plains to the Arkansas River, visiting en route the famous Pawnee Rock, followed the Arkansas down to Great Bend, then north into the valley of the Smoky Hill near Ellsworth, and from there east to the vicinity of Salina.

It was on this trip that Lester Ward found a new species of fossil eucalyptus leaf, which he very kindly named in my honor, *Eucalyptus gouldii,* so that I then had two scientific children. Since that time, a number of fossils have had the specific name *gouldii* attached to them, practically all of them being specimens which I had collected and had then sent to specialists for identification.

The last winter I was in college, 1898–99, I taught in the Winfield High School. I was glad to do so, although it meant a strenuous winter's work. I arose at five o'clock in the morning, studied my lessons, went to college, attended one class, caught the horse-drawn street car for the high school building a mile away, and taught three science classes before noon. By making special arrangements with my teachers I was able to do the rest of my college work in the afternoon.

I had now been in Southwestern for seven years. When I

66

Charles N. Gould, the budding professor, as he began his duties at the University of Oklahoma, September 16, 1900.

Van Vleet's field party, 1900; Roy Hadsell, left; Paul J. White, sitting; Gould, right.

Field party on the Salt Plains among the Gypsum Hills, Blaine County, 1900.

came from Kingman County, fresh from the wide-open spaces, I was deficient in everything except the common branches, and throughout my entire college course, I was always making up back work. Southwestern is a denominational school, and, following tradition, has always placed particular stress on the languages. A certain amount of Latin and of either Greek or German was then required for graduation. Oh, the weary hours I spent "grinding out" Latin and German. I had four years of Latin, three of German, one of French, and one of Greek. As I look back on my college life, I believe that this time was practically wasted, and that I might have been much better employed in taking studies which would have been of more lasting benefit to me and would have prepared me for my life's work. I believed then, and my later experience in a state university has strengthened the belief, that a super-abundance of required language, mathematics, or of any other subject, does not make for broad training or intellectual culture. I am and have always been a thorough believer in the elective system in college work. I have heard arguments *ad infinitum, ad nauseatum,* which have been worn threadbare by long years of use and misuse, attempting to prove that only by means of much Latin or much Greek or much something else "is educational salvation wrought." My experience has been that there is as much of educational and cultural value in a thorough knowledge of oak roots, or roots of the corn plant, as of Greek roots or cube roots. Experience has taught me that it is not the kind of roots, but the kind of digging that counts.

However, I had conscientiously ground through the various required courses, taking as many electives as were permitted, spending every summer in the field and every winter when I did not have to teach school to make money in digging out the various necessary branches, until finally I had completed the required work and was ready to graduate. My class was that of

1899. There were nine of us in the class, seven men and two women. One of the women was Miss Madeline Southard who has spent her life in missionary and evangelistic work. The other became the wife of a Methodist minister. Of the seven men, six were Methodist preachers, good, capable, honest fellows who have done their work in the world and done it well.

I was the only black sheep in the flock. While the other eight were centering their thoughts on things celestial, I was "of the earth earthy." Literally, my thoughts went downward. The brethren used to be greatly concerned about me, and held prayer meetings in my behalf. They seemingly could not understand how anyone who had had the advantages of the training that I had enjoyed could be anything but a preacher. I sometimes say that I came within *one* of being a preacher myself. My first degree, Bachelor of Science, was conferred by President Place in June, 1899.

By this time, I had begun to realize the possibilities which lay before me, and I began to be ambitious to succeed in my chosen profession. I set for myself three tasks, three objectives, to be attained. First, I resolved that I would some day occupy the chair of geology in some state university; second, I hoped to become state geologist of some state; and third, I determined to know as thoroughly as one might know, in the course of his life, the geology and mineral resources of the southern part of the Great Plains and the Southwest.

Within ten years of graduation, I had achieved the first two of these ambitions. I had organized the Department of Geology at the University of Oklahoma and had been appointed state geologist of Oklahoma. The third objective, to know the geology of the great Southwest, has occupied my best endeavors for more than forty years.

I had always hoped that, on graduating from Southwestern, I might attend the University of Kansas at Lawrence for a year, and there receive my master's degree. My good friend, Samuel Williston, had always taken a fatherly interest in my work, and had several times promised that he would try to have a place for me at the university when I graduated from Southwestern. By this time I had come to realize that, after all, the training one receives in the undergraduate work at a small denominational college is at best only preparatory and of little benefit for one who has ambitions to become a specialist in a scientific career. I was very anxious for post-graduate work such as I had hoped to get at the University of Kansas. I wrote Williston, asking if he could have a place for me the next year, and was much disappointed to learn that the only position available had been promised to one of his own students, E. H. Sellards, who was then specializing in fossil leaves of the Permian period.

This left me without a position for the next year. I wrote letters to several schools, trying to secure a place, and was gratified to receive a courteous letter from Professor Erwin H. Barbour, professor of geology at the University of Nebraska. He needed a man to work up a collection of fossil leaves. Two years with Lester Ward had given me a liking for fossil leaves. I had helped to make extensive collections of leaves from the Dakota formation of Cretaceous age in central Kansas. The same formations passed through Nebraska and many leaf fossils have been found there.

Professor Barbour was one of the best museum men in America, and he had in the museum a considerable collection of Dakota fossil leaves. The greater part of them had never been identified nor named. He offered me a fellowship in the University of Nebraska at a salary of three hundred dollars for the college year if I would agree to spend the summer in collecting fossil leaves and then come to Lincoln and spend the school year in identifying the specimens. This was exactly what I was looking for, and I wrote accepting the offer.

69

I secured a covered wagon and camp equipment at Winfield and started north across Kansas and Nebraska. On this trip I was accompanied by a schoolmate, Roy Hadsell, a graduate of the Normal Department of Southwestern, who later was for many years professor of English at the University of Oklahoma. We traveled from Winfield to Saline County, where Ward and I had collected, and there we secured many fossils from the Dakota sandstone. Thence north through Lincoln, where I first caught a glimpse of the university. From there, we went north and collected from numerous exposures on the bluffs of Missouri River above Omaha, as far as Sioux City, Iowa, and the southeast corner of South Dakota. I returned to Lincoln and enrolled in the university. During the summer I had sent in from the field about one hundred boxes of fossil leaves.

I have always looked back with much pleasure on the winter spent at the University of Nebraska. Professor Barbour is one of the finest gentlemen I have ever known, an inspiring teacher and a most loyal friend. C. A. Fisher held a fellowship in the department and taught classes in mineralogy. I enrolled in botany in classes under Professor F. E. Clements, who was assistant to Professor Charles E. Bessey, the noted botanist. Professor Bessey was acting chancellor that year, and much to my disappointment, I was unable to take work under him.

The greater part of my work consisted in chiseling out leaves and in classifying and naming them. I had several thousand specimens, including a few that were species new to science. I named something like twenty new species. Professor Barbour's encouragement, his advice and sympathy made my work a pleasure. During the winter I drew the three hundred dollars stipend for my fellowship in monthly installments of thirty dollars per month, lived on twenty-five dollars, and sent home five dollars to help out my sister who was still in college at Winfield.

Two men with whom I was most intimate were C. A. Fisher

and W. D. Hunter, an assistant in entomology. The three of us formed what we called "The Triumvirate," which was a league, offensive and defensive, against the rest of the human race, chiefly for the purpose of making puns and for keeping up what Mark Twain once called "a reviving state of oneryness."

There were no officers, no meetings, no duties, no dues, nothing but three exuberant young men in their late twenties who were bent on extracting from an unwilling and unsympathetic world as much as possible of the joy of living.

Hunter collected and identified beetles and other bugs, Fisher instructed young Cornhuskers in mineralogy, and I chiseled fossil leaves out of Dakota sandstone. We were all three very happy, very ambitious, and as poor as the proverbial church mice.

Along in the spring we all became very anxious. We each wanted a job. We needed a job. In fact, we had to have a job. And we did the thing that young collegians have always done; we sent applications far and wide, acquainting various university and government authorities with the fact that our valuable services were available and might be secured if proper financial arrangements were forthcoming.

We did more. We agreed among ourselves that the first member of the Triumvirate to connect with a payroll should thereupon stand the other two fellows a square meal.

Hunter won out. Along in May he secured a position for the next year. According to agreement, he took Fisher and me down to the Lincoln Hotel and bought us a fifty-cent dinner. I'd been eating fifteen-cent meals off restaurant stools so long that this dinner tasted mighty good.

In June, 1900, we graduated and scattered to various places. Hunter went to the Bureau of Entomology in Washington, but soon after was sent to Texas to investigate the boll weevil that had recently crossed the Rio Grande. Fisher went first to Yale, later took a position with the U. S. Geological Survey, and soon worked up to be assistant chief of the Fuel Division. I came to Oklahoma and organized the Department of Geology at the University of Oklahoma, a territorial institution just eight years old.

For some years thereafter our paths did not cross. Busy men we were; perhaps too busy to take account of the better things of life, and our friendship was permitted to drift.

But in 1910, we all found ourselves in Washington. By that time, Hunter was an authority on the cotton boll weevil. Fisher was learning all there was to know about the fuel resources of the nation, and I had become state geologist of Oklahoma.

Fisher and I happened to meet at the Geological Survey building. After renewing old acquaintance, we started out to find Hunter. We finally located him in a little cubby hole at the end of a long corridor in the Department of Agriculture building on the Mall. After we had pounded each other on the back and called each other chosen names, long forgotten, Fisher and I commandeered Hunter and made him stand the price of another dinner. This time it was served among the élite at the Cosmos Club. The three aspiring young assistants had all arrived.

Hunter continued his work on the boll weevil and became one of the most eminent economic entomologists in the world. He died several years ago from pneumonia contracted in the field, a soldier of science who gave his life in the line of duty. Fisher resigned from government service and for many years lived in Denver where he prospered in his chosen profession as consulting geologist and petroleum engineer, a fine, virile type of scientist and businessman. He died in 1930 of angina pectoris.

So of the members of the Triumvirate that flourished on the campus at Nebraska in 1900, I only am left.

At the end of the year's work at the University of Nebraska,

I received the degree of Master of Arts. During the year I had become a member of Sigma Xi, the honorary scientific fraternity. I have always regarded the winter's work under the guidance of Professor Barbour as one of the high spots in my life. For the first time I was brought into direct personal contact for a considerable period of time with a number of scientific men of high intellectual ability and special training, and the association and example of these men gave me an outlook on life which I have never forgotten.

While living in Kingman County, we had known a family named Bucklin, who lived not far from us. Mother and Mrs. Bucklin had been enthusiastic workers in the W.C.T.U. After we moved to Winfield, the son, George, attended college and boarded with Mother. Later he came to the University of Oklahoma as private secretary to the first president, David Ross Boyd.

I had known George intimately and had once remarked to him that I should like to teach geology in the University of Oklahoma. As the University grew, it became advisable to establish a department of geology. Bucklin suggested my name and Boyd instructed him to write me asking if I would come to Norman for the next year for a modest salary. This plan suited me, and at the Christmas holidays I ran down to Norman, had an interview with President Boyd and Professor Van Vleet, the head of biological sciences, and it was decided that I would spend the summer of 1900 in the field as a member of a camping party, without salary, and in September come to the University and undertake the organization of a geological department.

CHAPTER 4

ACROSS OKLAHOMA
BY COVERED WAGON

THE TWENTIETH CENTURY was only half a year old. Four young men in their late twenties or early thirties, carefree and happy, full of the joy of living, seeking new things, adventuring into the unknown, started out in a covered wagon for a summer's work, exploring Oklahoma.

And what an adventure it was! True, the days were sometimes hot and dusty, the water was often bad, mosquitoes whined and chiggers bit both by day and by night, but what cared we? These things were unimportant; they meant nothing in our young lives, they were all in the day's work. There was always something new around the corner, something unexpected over the next hill.

Our chief concern was locating, each night, the three requisites of a good camp, grass, wood and water. Incidentally, we were trying to find out what Oklahoma possessed in the way of birds, flowers, and rocks.

All four of us were inveterate and incurable punsters, two were addicted to the vice of doggerel, and one was even suspected of being a poet.

David Ross Boyd, the first president of the University of Oklahoma, and Henry E. Asp, the president of the Board of Regents, had succeeded in having passed by the Territorial

Legislature a bill establishing a Territorial Geological and Natural History Survey. The sum of money provided for the maintenance of this survey was two hundred dollars a year, later increased to three hundred dollars. According to the provisions of the bill, the professor of biology at the University was designated as *ex officio* territorial geologist, and accordingly Professor A. H. Van Vleet assumed these duties. The first year's appropriation was spent for the purchase of equipment, including a team of horses, a covered wagon, a tent, and some pots, pans, and cots.

It had been decided to put a party in the field during the summer of 1900, but Professor Van Vleet found himself under the embarrassment of having a Geological Survey without a geologist. This situation was corrected when President Boyd's secretary, George Bucklin, recommended his friend Gould for the position, as has been mentioned.

So I came to the University from my home at Winfield on June 10 to meet Professor Van Vleet, who had asked me to locate a botanist and a cook to go with the party. I had two friends, former students at Winfield, whom I suggested, Paul J. White as botanist, and Roy Hadsell as cook. These men were instructed to meet us at Orlando.

After four days in Norman assembling the outfit, we started north and camped the first night near Belle Isle between Oklahoma City and Britton. The man on whose farm we were camped wanted to sell us his claim for two thousand dollars, but neither of us had that much money. The second night we camped near Guthrie, then the capital of Oklahoma Territory, where we went to the office of Governor Barnes in order to secure a letter of introduction to the people of the Territory. Governor Barnes was not in the office, but his secretary, Fred L. Wenner, wrote us a letter commending us to the good graces of all the people of Oklahoma. The next night we drove to

Orlando and made camp on the school grounds, where we were joined by White and Hadsell.

When a prairie storm swept in from the northwest the first night, we received our initiation into camp life. The tent stakes had not been driven securely, so one of the party had to go out in the rain, with his nightshirt flapping about his legs, and drive the stakes deeper so that the wind would not blow the tent over. Even then it was almost carried away. All four of us had to hang on to the tent poles for half an hour until the fury of the storm had passed. We were thoroughly drenched, and spent the next day drying our bedding and clothing. Some of the cook's tin dishes were found strung out for a quarter of a mile to the south.

It was on this trip that I first collected fossil reptiles in Oklahoma. While we were camped at Orlando, we met a local blacksmith, a natural collector, one of those men who is always hunting minerals and "specimens." He told us of a place a mile or so out of town where one might find petrified teeth and bones. We went with him, and in the side of a red clay bank near the road, we found teeth, vertebrae, plates, spines, rib bones, and leg bones of small animals, some still imbedded in the red clay and others weathered out on the slope below.

We collected for half a day and secured several hundred fragments. These were sent for identification to Professor Williston. He afterwards visited the locality with me, and since that time scores of geologists and paleontologists have collected there. Bones of the reptiles from the Orlando locality have later been sent to the principal museums of the United States and Europe.

Some of the world's first reptiles saw the light of day in what is now Oklahoma and Texas. In the development of vertebrates, or backboned animals, the reptiles hold an intermediate position. Lower in the scale of life are fishes and amphibia, and higher are birds and mammals. Paleontologists have found that higher forms were derived from the lower ones in the natural course of life development. Certain types of fishes developed into amphibia, and amphibia in time gave rise to primitive reptiles, from which sprang the birds and mammals.

Before the time when the red beds of western Oklahoma and Texas were being laid down in ancient seas, the dominant types of life were amphibia. Not the inconspicuous, harmless salamanders, toads and frogs as we have today in Oklahoma, but huge creatures with sharp teeth, long spines, and bony plates, provided with weapons of defense, able to make their way in the world and defend themselves against their enemies. If you can imagine a toad half as large as an ox, armed with spines and sharp teeth, you will get a faint idea of what some of these creatures looked like.

It was during Permian times that the transition between the amphibia and the reptiles took place. Later, the reptiles developed rapidly. During the next two or three geological ages, they became very large, and in Jurassic and Cretaceous times, culminated in the huge dinosaurs, some of them eighty feet long, among the largest animals that ever lived on the earth.

Leaving Orlando we drove north to Perry and inspected a "copper mine" which had been reported a few miles north of town. The copper proved to be streaks of blue shale.

From Perry we went southeast to Stillwater and visited the campus of the Oklahoma Agricultural and Mechanical College. At that time A. C. Scott was president, and all the instruction was given in one building, now known as Old Central. We went still farther east, seeking the eastern edge of the red beds, and trying to locate ledges of limestone. Near Council Creek we found a four-foot ledge. We camped one night near Ingalls,

77

the scene of the famous battle with the Dalton gang of outlaws seven years earlier. Backtracking through Stillwater to Perry, we made Sunday camp.

It was here that the botanist discovered that his trousers needed repairs. At nightfall, as he sat on a roll of blankets in the tent, plying needle and thread, his mischievous companions collaborated in concocting the following effusion, which next day was chanted to his muttered disgust as the wagon jolted westward across the prairie:

"WHEN P.J. PATCHED HIS PANTS"
When Paul J. patched his pants
The birds stopped singing,
And darkness came, and lamps were lighted,
The stars came out,
And frogs began to croak,
When P.J. patched his pants.

When Paul J. patched his pants
The flies all went to bed;
Mosquitoes came and whined,
Beetles buzzed and hummed,
Sad dogs began to bark on distant farms,
When P.J. patched his pants.

When Paul J. patched his pants
He wrapped him in a blanket red,
And sat within his tent and sewed;
The while the passerby looked in and smiled;
Methinks they thought they saw an Indian chief,
When P.J. patched his pants.

We drove west to Enid where camp was made at Government Springs in the outskirts of the city. These springs were a famous watering place on the old Chisholm Cattle Trail, over which, during the eighteen seventies and eighties, great herds of Texas longhorn cattle had been driven to northern markets. When the Rock Island Railroad built south from Kansas to Texas, it followed the old Chisholm Trail.

After laboring for two days through the jackoaks and sand hills that lie north of the Cimarron River, we at last reached Cleo Springs, near the mouth of Eagle Chief Creek. Filling our water can and canteens, we forded the Cimarron and made for the Glass Mountains, ten miles distant. This was my first view of these gypsum-covered buttes, which for many years had been famous landmarks on the plains. These buttes are outliers of the Gypsum Hills six miles to the southwest.

We found no good water near the Glass Mountains and, after one day spent in exploring, returned to Cleo Springs to enjoy the cool shade, the pure water, and the songs of birds. In those days, western Oklahoma offered no more pleasant retreat.

Rumors had reached us of a certain Big Salt Plain, two days' drive to the north. Early next morning we broke camp and started north along Eagle Chief. Night camp was on the flat prairie on the divide between streams flowing south into the Cimarron and north into the Salt Fork. Next day we kept on traveling north. It was a hot, midsummer day, with a strong south wind; vegetation was drying up and crops were suffering from lack of rain. Mirages shimmered on the horizon, lifting, spreading, dissolving, changing, never the same, a continuous confusion of impossibilities, tempting one to follow.

Along in the afternoon, on topping a low hill over the rolling prairie, we saw away to the north what we thought was a new kind of mirage. It glistened white in the sun and did not move. We wondered and speculated as to what it might be. In the course of an hour as we drew nearer, it began to dawn on us that we were looking, not at a mirage, but at the Salt Plain. An

79

hour before sundown, we watered our team, filled our water can at a windmill, and drove to the edge of the Salt Plain to camp.

I have seen this Salt Plain scores of times since, but never without a thrill; and never shall I forget the feeling that came over me at the time of my first view. This plain is absolutely unique. There is nothing else like it anywhere east of the Rocky Mountains. What we saw was a flat basin, stretching away to the north as far as the eye could see, rimmed with low red hills. Later we learned that the length of the plain, north and south, is about twelve miles, and that the width, east and west, is six miles.

The plain is as flat as a floor. The small streams that flow into it from the sides spread out and disappear. It was as white as a snow field, the surface covered with a thin incrustation of salt crystals. I have since seen the plain after a heavy rain, when the water has dissolved the salt and the color is a reddish brown. It is practically barren of vegetation. After supper we took a spade and dug holes in the soft dirt that makes up the glistening plain, and in five minutes the holes were nearly filled with strong salt brine.

In the morning we started to drive across the plain to the west side, following some old wagon tracks. The wind began to rise and soon the air was filled with fine salt crystals, which caused our eyes to smart and burn so that we had to take turns driving. We were more than an hour crossing the plain, and before we were across, the horses were sneezing and shaking their heads and each of us had a handkerchief over his eyes.

From the Salt Plain the trail led west across the prairie, where later was built the town of Cherokee, and on to Alva, where the Santa Fe Railroad crossed the Salt Fork of the Arkansas. My most vivid recollections of Alva are the horses tied to the hitching posts around the square, and water wagons selling drinking water hauled from springs north of Salt Fork at a nickel a drink or a quarter a bucketful. We crossed Salt Fork and made camp among the sand hills, where we spent the next day, the Fourth of July. I took this opportunity to study the sand dunes which are so common north of many of the streams in western Oklahoma.

We followed the old Camp Supply Trail that led over the hills from Alva. At this time the homesteader had reached western Woods County, and near the edge of the Gypsum Hills we found a nester nailing up his shack. His family was still camped in a covered wagon down by the creek, where his wife was spreading the family wash on bushes to dry.

While the horses rested, we talked to the man. He seemed willing to visit, and we soon learned that he was from the Ozark Mountains in southern Missouri. We had quite a discussion as to whether or not Woods County was a better corn country than the one he had just left. He believed that it might be a better wheat country, but "he hadn't never raised no wheat."

This was ten years before I heard my good friend John Fields, director of the Experiment Station at the Oklahoma A. and M. College, say in a public address: "The farmers of western Oklahoma have been losing a million dollars a year betting the Lord that they lived in a corn country."

The trail we were following took us across the red hills, and a few miles beyond we came to a well-used camping place, and so knew that water must be near. Just under the hill we found a fine flow of water known throughout all that country as White Horse Spring.

That evening the cook spread our supper on a flat rock, and as the men were eating, I noticed beside my plate some small fossil shells. After supper I took my hammer and by cracking open the rocks in the low cliff above the camp, found that they were full of fossils. The other men joined me and we collected nearly a hundred pounds of fossil-bearing sandstone which we shipped to Norman. Several years later I named one of the red bed formations the "White Horse Sandstone," the type locality being at White Horse Spring where, on July 5, 1900, I found fossils in the rock at our camp.

Next morning we continued on the Camp Supply Trail, which we had been following since leaving Alva. Late that afternoon the wagon topped a hill and we could see for many miles in all directions. On to the west wound the trail that we were to travel all next day. Someone remarked that it looked like a big snake. And so, improvising as we jogged along, Hadsell and I thought out the following:

"THE TRAIL"

The trail leads up and the trail leads down
 And the trail winds in and out, around
Across the arroyo, and over the hill,
 By canyon and butte, and valley, still
The trail winds on like a giant snake
 Hunting its hole in the hills.

There are rocks on the hillside, and cattle hard by,
 The buzzard a speck in the open sky;
The coyote slinks through the tall, rank grass,
 And the prairie dogs bark as the travelers pass;
But the trail leads on like a giant snake
 Hunting its hole in the hills.

The lengthening shadows cross the plain,
 The camp site is chosen once again;
The coffee boils on the camp fire bright,
 The horses are picketed for the night;
Yet the trail leads on like a giant snake
 Hunting its hole in the hills.

President David Ross Boyd of the University of Oklahoma, 1903. His faculty included, among others, Vernon Louis Parrington, A. H. Van Vleet, Frederick Holmberg, Roy Hadsell, and Charles N. Gould.

First topographic party in the Arbuckle Mountains, 1909:
E. DeGolyer at the plane table, Key Wolf holding the rod.

The blankets are spread on the dewy sod
   Where a few years since the buffalo trod.
The night is passed in dreamless rest.
We rise with the dawn, but still to the west,
The trail leads on like a giant snake
   Hunting its hole in the hills.

Let me include here a few paragraphs from Roy Hadsell's diary:

July 7
"Still on the trail today; hoping to reach the Salt Plain of the Cimarron. Surrounding the plain on three sides are great cliffs one hundred feet high of red rock, topped by white gypsum ledges. As at the other salt plain we caught sight of it many miles back. Along the bottoms the grass is rich and hundreds of cattle fattened by it and by easy access to the salt plains, roam about. We looked in vain for good water at noon, so camped by a little slough and had our dinner. Gould and White roamed about for salt plants while I had coffee boiling. Dr. Van Vleet hunted birds. Soon after dinner we struck across the plain and were nearly all afternoon in doing it because there was so much that was interesting. Dr. Van Vleet got some salt water birds that are common only on sea coasts. The crossing was difficult because the salt field reflected the sun till our eyes ached, and because of the quicksand through which the team had to pull the wagon. These western streams look so innocent, but one dare not stop a single moment in crossing them. Gould drove the horses, White and I pushed, and at length we got safely across the Cimarron. The salt springs were on the south side, pure, clear-looking water bubbled up in places. In the little ditches in the sand it looked more like glass than water,

but it was bitter with salt. Put your finger in the water a moment, then hold it in the air and it becomes white from the evaporation. So saturated is the water that great crystals of salt are being deposited all the time. Grass stems gather beautiful salt crystals. I intended to take a bath in one of the little puddles but the boys coaxed me out of the notion. After getting a number of pictures we struck on west. Dr. V. tried hard to get a shot at a flock of long-billed curlews but instead brought down some hawks before he quit. About camping time we entered a prairie dog town of probably two hundred acres. The little fellows, sitting upright, kept up a continuous chirping. At six I had supper ready. Dr. V. who was hunting birds and snakes came in for his supper about sundown. I wished for a picture of our camp at sundown, south of us and winding to east and north the little creek, our tent and covered wagon under an elm tree on a flat plot of prairie dog town. West of us the red hills with their curvy outline and long slopes over which the sun slowly tumbles, leaving his path on hill and sky a thousand colors.

July 8

"Because we are in a cattle country where houses and wells are days' drives apart and because we are nearly out of supplies, we decided to move a few miles today instead of resting as is usually our plan on Sunday. Leisurely we took the road. We all disliked leaving our beautiful camp. Up from the valley we emerged, our team trailing along. In the distance a freighter hauling on the trail from Dodge to Fort Supply comes in view. Six horses and two wide-wheeled covered wagons, one fastened behind the other, soon pass us, a little train. Again a ranch wagon, a herd of ranch ponies and probably a thousand cattle attended by four typical cowboys float past, a nod and a "good morning" and we pass like ships on the sea. How much the vast prairie must resemble the ocean, and how little imagination it takes to people it with Indians and buffaloes. Several miles to the east are the Wildcat Mounds, looking like mountains in the distance, where a murder was reputed to have been committed and the victim buried. We have been in sight of them for days. At the sides of the old trail we follow there are buffalo wallows often filled with water, from which we dip water for the team. An arrowhead picked up on the hills, and the legend of deer hunts right in this region make the desert an entire oasis for me. We stopped at a ranch about eleven o'clock. A fine spring emptying into a pond furnishes our horses and our canteens this time. Eight miles farther, we are told, is a good spring, and we drive over the hilliest country not to be called mountains I have ever seen. Tired, dirty and hungry, until at two o'clock to find a neat little house under a hill near a heavily wooded stream where a stream of clear water winds through white sand, near which we can camp and be happy. If you want to appreciate your blessings travel through a salt plains country two days with only warm water in a tin canteen, and see how your heart leaps at a spring like this. Tired and hungry though we were, every fellow had his joke and fun, and at dinner we were merry enough to grace a feast. We had a part of the day left to have a Sunday cleanup; so we washed our clothes, and C.N. and I had a bath, or at least we wallowed in the creek. I go to bed dog tired but glad of a chance to live the life.

July 9

"Today brought us to Fort Supply. We drove around in the "deserted village" and at last found water and a little store. One is surprised, after several days of prairie driving with never a house in sight, to come upon a little city, with water system, phone lines, etc. But the glory of the fort has departed since it was abandoned nine years ago, and now only a few of the buildings that were used, barracks and officers quarters, stand to tell the traveler of the days that are gone. The others left me in camp just outside the fort and drove off to the hills looking for fossils. I visited the cemetery and the fort, and tried to satisfy my curiosity. The boys came home about six. After supper while Gould was packing his fossils, White and I went over to the fort for some water and boxes. We roamed in the moonlight through deserted buildings. I heard a guitar somewhere (there are about fifteen families here now) and coaxed White to go by the house. I was cheeky enough to give my box to White and go in and sit on the porch. Played and sang awhile, then back to camp to hear the jokes at my expense. Then after a swim, to bed."

From Camp Supply, we drove over the sand hills to Woodward, laid in supplies, and started southeast toward Curtis, the Gypsum Hills, and the Bat Caves.

We made camp on a little level prairie above the head of a canyon in eastern Woodward County. We picked that particular spot because not fifty yards away was the entrance to a bat cave. The country is full of ledges of white gypsum, and the caves had been worn out by the action of water in the red clay beneath the gypsum. Gnarled cedars were wedged in the crevices of the rocks, sage brush nodded in the evening breeze. The campfire was soon burning, the horses were led down the trail to water, and then picketed for the night. The coffee pot bubbled, bacon sizzled in the pan, and as it came on dusk, we spread our supper on the grass. Does anything ever taste quite so good as a camp supper after a hard day's ride in a jolty wagon?

Before we had finished, someone yelled, "The bats are coming out," and we all left our supper uneaten to rush down to the edge of the canyon. Sure enough, the bats *were* coming out, in a perfect stream. Tens of thousands, hundreds of thousands of bats. There was no way of estimating their number. Uncounted myriads poured from the dark mouth of the cave, like a cloud of black smoke. We stood in the gathering darkness watching the stream pour forth. For half an hour, until it became too dark to distinguish individuals, we wondered and speculated as to the strange thing we were watching.

That night I spread my blankets on the grass under the stars at the edge of the canyon, right above the mouth of the cave; the odor of cedar, sage brush, and wood smoke from the dying fire was with me. The moan of a coyote on a distant hill lulled me to sleep. Can anyone anywhere sleep as soundly as stretched out on the ground after a hard day in a jolty wagon?

When the dawn was yet gray in the east, I awoke. The bats were returning. Not in a stream as they had left at dusk, but singly, apparently dropping from the sky. It was raining bats. The air was suddenly full of bats. Each individual dropped like a stone from some invisible place in the upper air, poised an instant at the mouth of the cave, then with a flirt and a flutter and a tiny squeak, disappeared into the darkness of the cave.

For nearly an hour they kept coming. The sun peeped over the eastern horizon, and the dewdrops became a million diamonds. Its coming was the signal for all remaining bats to report home. A last contingent sifted down out of the sky and found their way up the canyon into the cave.

The campfire burned, coffee boiled, breakfast was eaten and blankets rolled. The horses were led down the steep cow trail to the creek for water, and the party made ready to start. The last thing before climbing into the driver's seat, I stepped down to the edge of the canyon. The sun was half an hour high and the dew-diamonds had disappeared. A few belated stragglers were still blundering their way up the canyon to their home in the cave.

Leaving the Gypsum Hills we journeyed south, crossed the

North Canadian at Richmond, now a ghost town, and on to the bluffs of the Canadian north of Taloga. The river was running high and we crossed with some difficulty and made camp on the south bank.

It was here that I first made the acquaintance of the most treacherous of all the streams of the plains, the Canadian. I have since learned that from the Missouri to the Rio Grande none exceeds the Canadian either in sudden rises in the volume of water that for short periods flows down the channel, or for the depth of the quicksand. Usually the Canadian is a dry sand bed half a mile wide, but every so often, without warning, a boiling, seething wall of foaming, muddy water fed by cloudbursts upstream sweeps down the channel carrying everything before it.

About sundown, a homesteader came driving along with his wife and several small children in a covered wagon. A tenderfoot he must have been, because he drove hub-deep into the stream directly and then stopped to water his team. The wheels began to sink into the quicksand, and when the horses tried to start the wagon, it didn't budge. We stood on the bank and watched the performance. The horses began to rear and plunge and flounder; one of them got his feet over the wagon tongue and fell down and was about to drown. The man jumped out, unhooked the tugs, and cut the breast strap, and the horse finally scrambled to the bank.

By this time the woman and children were screaming. We rolled our trousers above the knee, waded in, and carried them ashore. We also rescued the quilts and other household goods, started a fire and helped the family dry out and make camp on the river bank. We tried to persuade the man to secure help and get his wagon out of the quicksand before dark, but he " 'lowed it would be easier to do the work in the mawnin'."

Morning came. The river had risen during the night. About three feet of the top of the wagon bows were above the water.

The wagon, bed and all, had settled into the quicksand. That was over forty years ago. It is there today.

From Taloga we kept on south to Arapaho, where we had the horses shod, and then drove several miles west where we found, in the hills along Barnitz Creek, large deposits of fossil oyster shells. In 1853, Jules Marcou, the geologist for the Whipple military expedition crossing the plains, had found the same deposit of shells along this creek, which he called Comet Creek.

These fossils represent a geological period, the Comanche, or Lower Cretaceous, when the water of the Gulf of Mexico transgressed western Oklahoma, forming an ocean which extended north across the Great Plains almost to the Arctic. The shells which we found on Barnitz Creek belonged to the same species as those which Williston, Hill, Ward, Stanton, and I had collected at Belvidere and in Clark County, Kansas, several years before. Boxing a collection of oyster shells, we returned to Arapaho for Sunday camp.

Some men and boys who lived near by dropped into camp and we soon became acquainted. It was here that I first heard of the "three questions" which were common in Oklahoma in an early day. The first question was, "Where you from?" the second, "What was your name back there?" and the third, "Why did you leave?" It was not always considered in the best of taste to insist on an answer to the third question.

One of the young men at our Arapaho camp had set the idea to music. One verse follows:

Oh, what was your name in the States?
Was it Thompson or Johnson or Bates?
Did you murder your wife
And flee for your life?
Say, what was your name in the States?

89

A popular song in which the whole crowd indulged was:

Oh, here's to G county, the land of the free;
The home of the bed bug, the tick, and the flea.
We'll sing of her praises, and tell of her fame:
While starving to death on a government claim.

It should be explained that G county, of which Arapaho was the county seat, was one of the "lettered counties" of Oklahoma. The name Custer was chosen at the first election.

After some insistence, the poet of our party gave the crowd his latest triumph:

Oh, this is the tale of the ant-a-mire,
    That crawled into our sugar jire,
And ate, and ate, and ate his best,
    And then rushed back and told the rest
Who came in troops from near and far
    To war upon our sugar jar.

There were more verses, but this sample should suffice. Again I quote Hadsell:

July 12

"A day's rest put both men and horses in good spirits so we start another week. Reached some gypsum caves about ten o'clock, where we explored a cave, then journeyed on to Weatherford. This is the end of the Choctaw railroad and since several inland towns depend on this road, the trail to the west was well-beaten by freighters' wagons. Weatherford must be a tough town, the end of the railroad, and a market for this border land. While the other men were shipping some boxes I watched a family of Cheyenne Indians break camp. The two men stood around doing nothing while the two women hitched up the ponies and piled pots, harness, and dirty bed clothes all of a jumble into the wagons, and they all drove away.

"We went east of Weatherford to the Wichita Reservation. Fifty miles south we could see the blue outline of some of the high peaks of the Wichita Mountains. Tonight we are in camp on the 'lone prairie' in the 'Caddo country.' To the north, across the fence, eighteen hundred cattle are grazing. Some hills form our camp's south border, but the rest is prairie.

"Night comes down differently on the prairie than anywhere else. No lights twinkle out, for there are no houses within ten miles. Neither do bells ring. The bull bat dives down with his hoarse croak. The katydid and the cricket keep up an incessant chirp. We can hear the horses at their picket ropes as they munch, munch the grass. Across the fence, the cattle mope along, dark objects in the gathering dusk. The stars come out and so broad is the expanse of the heavens there seem to be millions more than common.

"These are the sounds, and these are the things one sees. All else is quiet, and peace—peace that sinks in as you roll in your blanket with your face to the sky."

Our camp had been among the Caddo County Buttes six miles south of the town of Hydro. The easternmost of these buttes had been named Rock Mary in 1853 by some officers of the Whipple military expedition which, a few years after the Mexican War, set out from Helena, Arkansas, to find a feasible route for a railroad across the southwestern part of the country to the Pacific Ocean.

Since leaving Taloga, we had been on the south side of the Canadian. Crossing again to the north side at Bridgeport, we continued north, passing a few miles west of Geary, crossed the

North Canadian near Watonga, and still farther northeast to the crest of the Gypsum Hills.

During the summer I had sent an occasional note to Fred S. Barde, of Guthrie, who for many years had been the Oklahoma correspondent for the *Kansas City Star,* who had asked me to send him occasional notes on our trip through Oklahoma. The following excerpts from an article which was published in the *Star* under date of August 13, 1900, will describe our experience among the jackoaks, the Gypsum Hills, and Salt Plains of Blaine County:

"We had been traveling all the afternoon through the sand hill, jack-oak country, northeast of Watonga. If there is anything more monotonous than a day's travel through a jack-oak forest, I have never found it. There is such a feeling of being shut in. In comparison, even the much-discussed monotony of the plains falls into insignificance. On the plains there is at least a wide range of vision. There the horizon is a circle of seemingly infinite circumference, of which you are the center. The sky is a vast dome across which fleecy clouds jog slowly like prairie schooners of the air. On the horizon one may always see something to break the everlasting sameness, a covered wagon with white canvas top, like a ship at sea—a prairie schooner. Or it may be a sentinel butte, or only a tree, now a herd of cattle or a solitary horseman, or perchance it is a mirage shimmering in the distance. Far away groves appear and vanish, and hill and plain and valley pass kaleidoscope-like across the vision, while near at hand the prairie grass or sagebrush, interspersed with innumerable flowers, presents a variety of color and form to excite at least a passing interest.

"But among the jack oaks it is different. Jack oaks are jack oaks the world over. Always the same ragged, black trunks, the same dark-green, paddle-shaped leaves, the same half-dead, jagged branches; the whole thing too large for a shrub and too small for a respectable tree. The ground covering is the same too; a scant growth of bunch grass with a few sand hill sunflowers and other weeds, while the rest is sand, sand into which the wheels sink over the felloes and through which the tired horses drag the heavy wagon.

"Through this tangle of scrubby trees we had toiled for half a day. The team was tired and we were hot and dirty and hungry. We knew that somewhere to the north was a certain Salt Creek, our destination, and we imagined it to be like so many of the streams we had seen, a flat, sandy draw with a dry bed and perhaps a few cottonwoods along the banks.

"But about an hour before sundown, the jack oaks began to thin out. Soon they disappeared altogether, and we found ourselves on the high divide between the North Canadian and Cimarron rivers, overlooking the most picturesque bit of scenery which we had found in western Oklahoma. Away to the northeast lay the broad valley of the Cimarron, dotted with farmhouses, groves, and wheat stacks. Fifteen miles away a fringe of cottonwood marked the channel of the river. Thirty miles east could be seen the smoke of the Rock Island train at Hennessey; twenty-five miles to the north was Cleo at the mouth of Eagle Chief, opposite the Glass Mountain where we had camped three weeks earlier.

"At our feet lay the canyons of Salt Creek and its tributaries; not flat sand draws, but mighty chasms hundreds of feet deep carved by the action of water into the hills. The harder rock, which here gives tone to the erosion forms, consists of three ledges of massive, white crystal gypsum which lie level, one above the other. They are each from five to twenty feet thick and are separated by strata of red clay. They lie a hundred feet below the jack-oak country on the divide across which we had been traveling, and more than two hundred feet above the level of the Cimarron Valley. These are the gypsum ledges which out-crop as a continuous line for hundreds of miles through Kansas and Oklahoma into Texas.

"In the Salt Creek region, as in other localities, the strata, both below and above the ledges of gypsum, consist of red clay shale, throughout which are interspersed streaks or bands of green and blue. Seen from above, the color contrast is especially marked. At our back extends the almost black jack oak forest; below us are the red slopes, with the light green of the prairie grass and bands of blue and green shale. Farther down are the ledges of white gypsum, peeping up out of the canyons. Beyond the line of bluffs and canyons, the blood-red glow of the plowed lands, the golden yellow of the wheat, and the green quad-rangles of growing corn, all fading out to the sky line thirty miles away, present a contrast of color most unusual to a plainsman.

"We left the high divide and made camp on the plateau which caps the bluffs, and next day drove down into the valley in order to get a view of the canyons and cliffs from below. We skirted the foot of the bluffs looking up from below at the gyp-sum ledge nearly three hundred feet above us. One may often see half a mile up several canyons from the same spot. In one of them the Cheyenne Chieftain Roman Nose has his camp. Along the bottom lands the dwarfed, shaggy mesquite grows in patches. It is a desert-loving plant that finds its most congenial habitat in the desert country of New Mexico and Arizona. Here it has wandered far from home and is making a sturdy struggle for existence in these salt wastes.

"We followed up the main canyon of Salt Creek. The sandy bed of the creek is thoroughly impregnated with strong salt brine from several springs near its head. It is along the banks of this salt plain that several primitive salt plants have been located. The water is pumped from shallow wells sunk into the plain, and is evaporated in pans, the salt being sold to supply the local demand.

"From the point where Salt Creek leaves the hills the distance is about two miles to the head of the canyon. The bluffs rise nearly three hundred feet above the creek bed and at the top the two massive ledges of gypsum are scarcely a quarter of a mile apart.

"A mile upstream the canyon forks. Each branch is deep and narrow, with a stream of salt water flowing down its beds. We went up the north fork and pitched our tent in a little grove of oak and mesquite trees near a deserted salt plant. The canyon here narrows rapidly, and the cliffs become steeper. Huge boulders of gypsum, fifteen to twenty feet in diameter, which have fallen from the ledges at the top of the bluffs and rolled down the slopes, obstruct the bed. The bluffs are frequently precipitous for a hundred feet. Cedars climb the cliffs. Buzzards sail slowly overhead. At five o'clock the sun drops behind the canyon wall. Our supper is spread on a massive gypsum boulder. Sleep comes easily."

Kingfisher was our next port of call, then south along the Rock Island Railroad, past Okarche and Caddo Springs (now Concho) to Darlington and El Reno.

Again let me quote Hadsell:

"Near Moore, Norman in sight. August 1, 1900.

"Last night we filled our tent with straw from a stack and had a jolly sleep. Were in good spirits all day. The country around Kingfisher, El Reno, and Oklahoma City is a fine wheat region, with prosperous-looking farms, the best we have seen since leaving Enid. We passed southwest of Oklahoma City. We are simply driving home now, so nothing in the way of work comes before us. In the afternoon we got to singing; hymns are the only tunes we all know, and we can sometimes hit a chord together. Gould led out in true camp-meeting style and the rest of us chimed in. At several houses people came to the doors to see what kind of a show was coming. I suppose they thought ours was a gospel wagon. Camp was a mile west of Moore. White and I walked half a mile to a stack for straw for our beds. While we were not looking, Gould appropriated some of our straw from us for his bed, and then while he was puttering around the wagon, White slipped out and stole it all back again. At breakfast Gould bragged of how easy his bed was, but when he came to roll his blankets he found only about four straws on the ground.

August 2, 1900

"Today led us into Norman. We stopped for a few minutes at Moore where Dr. V. and I hoped to get shaved. We each had a six-weeks growth of beard. The barber said that by putting off an intended trip he guessed he could shave us, which remark made the Doctor angry, and so on we drove, came into Norman with our whiskers on, and at noon we pitched our tent on the University campus."

After remaining at Norman a few days, White, Hadsell and I started east to make a circle trip via Shawnee, Okmulgee, Sapulpa, Tulsa, and Pawhuska, and back to our homes at Winfield. Professor Van Vleet remained in Norman to arrange for the opening of term. The object of this latter part of the summer's trip was to try to find out how far south into Oklahoma and Indian Territory the limestone ledges extended. I knew that this rock occurred in the western part of the Osage country, for while I was a student at Winfield I had found limestone in the Osage Nation, and early on the trip we had found a single ledge near Council Creek a few miles east of Stillwater, but no one knew how far south it came.

So the three of us started out with the team and covered wagon across the jack-oak country of eastern Cleveland County and the western Potawatomi Indian Reservation. It is rough and hilly, much cut up with small streams and covered with scrub-oak and hickory timber. The old trails across the country had been fenced, and the new roads along the section lines varied from bad to worse. Clearings had been made in the timber and little fields planted to cotton and corn. The houses were chiefly one-room log cabins or board shacks.

For the first time we three Kansas boys saw women use the snuff stick, and somebody remarked that all the men chewed tobacco. As we jogged along on the rough, bumpy roads, talking about the country, the crops, and the people, a verse began to form in our minds. I believe it was Hadsell, the poet of the party, who first evolved the meter, "The men chew tobacco, and the women dip snuff." Someone else added another line and soon we had a quatrain which ran as follows:

Oh, it's down in the country of the Pott-o-wat-o-mies
Where the leaves grow green on the jack-oak trees.
If you travel through the country, you will learn it sure
    enough,
That the men chew tobacco and the women dip snuff.

That set us going and before long we had evolved a second verse something as follows:

The women wear sunbonnets, and the men plow cotton,
The going is tough and the roads are rotten,
When you travel 'cross the country you will find it mighty
    rough,
Where the men chew tobacco and the women dip snuff.

Plodding along that hot afternoon, we must have concocted a dozen stanzas, most of which I have forgotten, but another one comes to mind:

There are cows in the pasture, and pigs in the pen,
Chickens in the yard, a rooster and a hen.
Pulling through the sand the horses pant and puff,
Where the men chew tobacco and the women dip snuff.

We forded Little River at Big Jim Crossing, which had been named for the chief of one band of Absentee Shawnees, a tribe which had joined the Potawatomis and with them had received allotments of land. Big Jim, whose allotment was near by, represented the most conservative faction of the Shawnees. He would not cultivate the soil, believing that the earth was his mother, and he would not cut and disfigure his mother's face with the plow or spade.

After two days of jolting over the roads of the jack-oak country, we finally reached Tecumseh, named for the great chief of the Shawnee Indians, and thence drove north to Shawnee. My most vivid recollection of this town is that every second building on Main Street was a saloon. We crossed the northwest corner of the Seminole Nation, near the old Indian school, Econtuchka, and camped at Keokuk Falls, then a whisky town on the North Canadian River, where there was a water mill for grinding grain. The place had long been a ghost town.

Our route led east across the Creek Nation to Okmulgee. There were no towns on the way, and but few small farms. The site of Okemah was bald prairie. Okmulgee then consisted of a few shack houses grouped around the old Creek Capitol, a square, two-story, stone building. We made camp about two blocks north of the Capitol building, and in the morning a bunch of razorback shotes routed us out of our blankets. North of Okmulgee we met the Frisco Railroad building south from Sapulpa toward Texas. Sapulpa, being a railroad town, was then larger than Okmulgee. We made night camp near Taneha Mound, half way between Sapulpa and Tulsa, where, a few years later, was developed the northern extension of Glenn Pool, the first major oil field in Oklahoma.

On reaching the Arkansas at Tulsa, we found that the river was running full. There was no bridge and no one appeared to be crossing. We waited awhile on the south bank, hoping some-one would come along and ford the river, and finally White pulled off his shoes, socks, and trousers and waded in to see if the river was too deep to cross.

Just as he reached the middle of the stream a team drove up with a wagon containing father, mother, and the girls. They drove on across past Paul J. standing blushing, in water up to his knees.

At that time Tulsa had about two hundred and fifty people, living chiefly in wooden shacks near the Frisco depot. The larg-est house belonged to Chief Perryman of the Creeks; the Tulsa County courthouse was afterward built in his yard. We were offered town lots at Third and Main streets for two hundred dollars each. The man finally came down to one hundred twenty-five dollars, but none of us had that much money.

We visited the strip-pit coal mine at Dawson a few miles northeast of Tulsa. This was the first coal mine I had seen since leaving Ohio. Driving north, we crossed the Cherokee Nation, and near Skiatook crossed the line into the Osage Nation and followed the old Indian Trail up Bird Creek to Pawhuska. We walked up town to see what we could see.

At that time the Osages were among the most primitive of all the Indians in Oklahoma. Many of the full bloods still retained their ancient tribal customs. The men shaved the head except for a scalplock, which extended from the forehead to the back of the neck, and wore only a blanket, leggings, cotton shirt, and moccasins. Few of them pretended to work.

There were at that time two towns at Pawhuska; the white man's town, made up of several large stores, kept by licensed traders, with a dozen or two shops of various kinds, and the Indian town situated about a mile distant, which consisted of a collection of perhaps fifty or seventy-five tipis, bark-and-pole houses, and brush arbors.

Leaving Pawhuska, we started northwest to Winfield. All the way from Norman, the rocks had been chiefly sandstone and shale. Six miles west of Pawhuska we climbed out of Bird Creek Valley and encountered a heavy ledge known as the Pawhuska limestone, and from that point found limestone all the way to Winfield.

We remained at Winfield a few days while we packed and loaded our belongings, then started south in our covered wagon into Oklahoma, and to Norman.

CHAPTER 5

I TEACH GEOLOGY AT THE
UNIVERSITY OF OKLAHOMA

One lone building in a forty-acre field
With rows of little trees, waist high.
A faculty of seven,
Forward-looking and far-visioned men,
Willing to toil and hope and sacrifice.
Three hundred students,
Earnest, stalwart, young men and women,
From sodhouse, dugout, and cattle ranch
A hope of better things to be.

THIS WAS the University of Oklahoma when I came to the campus.

I began my class work in geology at the University in September, 1900; my salary the first year was four hundred dollars. At that time there were about three hundred students enrolled in the institution, sixty of whom were of college rank, the others being chiefly preparatory students. All of the work was carried on in one building. The forty-acre campus was bounded by Boyd, Asp, Brooks and Elm streets.

There were no rooms available for geology. I was allowed to place a desk in Professor Van Vleet's office. There was absolutely no equipment for carrying on the work of the department; no classrooms, no laboratories, no collections, no library, nothing but a young chap just out of college, turned loose on his own resources and permitted to sink or swim.

The first Territorial Legislature had established the University of Oklahoma at Norman. The original faculty consisted of four men: David Ross Boyd, president, who taught mathematics; Edwin DeBarr, who taught all the other sciences; W. N. Rice, who had the languages; and F. S. E. Amos, who carried the history and allied subjects. The first instruction was given in a building on Main Street in September, 1892, and the first building erected the same year.

At one of the early meetings of the Board of Regents, President Boyd suggested planting trees on the campus, but the regents would not agree to spend money on trees because, they said, trees would not grow on the upland prairie in Oklahoma. President Boyd then proposed to plant trees at his own expense.

He hired a patch of prairie sod broken out on the southeast corner of the campus where the Business Administration Building is now located and planted seedlings of elm, ash, and locust. When these had grown to be waist high, they were transplanted in rows around the campus and along the Boulevard, the north approach to the University. Very few of these original trees are still alive, old, gnarled, scraggy elms. Several of them may be seen back of the Business Administration Building.

Certain additions and changes had been made in the faculty so that at the turn of the century the teaching staff was as follows: David Ross Boyd, president; Edwin DeBarr, chemistry and pharmacy; J. S. Buchanan, history; J. F. Paxton, ancient language; F. S. Elder, mathematics; Vernon Louis Parrington, English; A. H. Van Vleet, biology; and Grace King, music.

Five additions were made to the faculty in 1900; namely, L. E. Cole, psychology; L. M. Upjohn, who started the Medical School; W. H. Matlock, modern languages; J. W. Sturgis, Latin; and Charles N. Gould, geology.

I had brought with me from Winfield my private library of about two hundred volumes, mostly textbooks and government reports, and after some months, I secured a carpenter to make a set of shelves to hold them. I also brought to Norman a number of fossils and rock specimens which I had collected in Kansas and Nebraska. There was no place to display this material, and it remained boxed until it was lost in the fire which destroyed the University building three years later.

My classes were held wherever a room could be found. The class in beginning geology met in the English room during a vacant hour. The class in physiography met in a corner of Professor Van Vleet's laboratory. The first year the enrollment in the department was not large. During the fall term I had one class with four students and one with six, and in the spring the enrollment in my largest class was nine.

Among the students who took geology during my first year at the University were the following: George Bucklin, Roy Hadsell, Kate Barbour, John T. Hefley, Lillie Miller, Mr. and Mrs. Roy Gittinger, E. M. Vanderslice, Milton J. Ferguson, Paul Mackey, Ray Crow, and C. C. Roberts. I enjoyed my first year's work, and apparently I had demonstrated the value of a department of geology to the University. At any rate, at the close of the school year, the Board of Regents raised my salary to $1,200.

During the summer of 1901, I obtained employment with the United States Geological Survey. Joseph A. Taff, who, for a number of years had been working in the coal fields of Indian Territory, engaged me as assistant in a field party. I joined his party at Westville, Cherokee Nation, near the Arkansas line, and we spent two months working out the geology and mapping the Tahlequah Quadrangle. The camp outfit consisted of a covered wagon, drawn by two heavy mules, and three saddle mules. Taff rode Jack, and my mule was Jinnie. George I. Adams, of the U. S. Geological Survey, was also a member of the party. The Tahlequah country is hilly and heavily timbered, and at that time was inhabited chiefly by full-blood Cherokees. Tahlequah, the old Cherokee capital, was a scattered village of a few hundred people, built near some fine springs.

It was during this trip that I first met my friend, Johnnie Walkingstick, a full-blood. He didn't like white men very much. I think that, as we became better acquainted, he came to like me, but I was never quite sure. With his old chum, Tom Sixkiller, he would squat in the shade of the smoke house for hours at a time, jabber away in Cherokee, and spit tobacco juice among the Jimson weeds, but when I tried to draw him into conversation in English, he would usually respond with a grunt.

The first time I saw Johnnie was one day when I suddenly came on his one-room cabin in a clearing as I was riding Jinnie, following a section line through the timber, checking contacts and mapping outcrops. He and his family were at dinner. In the middle of the table under a hickory tree in the back yard was a dishpan full of stewed blackberries; nothing else. Johnnie, Mrs. Johnnie, and half a dozen little Johnnies, each with a big spoon in his fist sat or stood around the table, eating blackberries directly out of the dishpan. Both the faces of the youngsters and the top of the table were liberally smeared with blackberry juice.

Johnnie had a grievance and thought it was a good reason for not liking white man's ways. Tom Sixkiller, his chum and lifetime friend, lived half a mile away alongside a mountain. A path, worn by countless bare feet during three generations, connected the two cabins, both of which were built hard by a mountain spring, where the fathers and grandfathers of both men had lived. After the Cherokee's land had been allotted, and some of it sold, a man from Missouri bought a forty-acre tract lying between the two cabins and fenced it, closing the path. At the same time a wagon road was opened along the section line over a hill. Johnnie disapproved.

He said, "White man heap blame fool. Fence up little road, my house, Tom's house. My father, his father, go see Tom's father, his father [the Cherokee language has no specific word for 'grandfather'], my father go long time, I go, now no can go. Open up big road over hill, down 'crost holler, up 'nother hill. Shut up little road, straight my house, Tom's house. Now must go over hill, see Tom. White man heap big fool."

On one of our trips Johnnie taught me how to build a fire. I had been camping on the plains and in the timber for so many years that I had the conceit to believe I knew all about camping and fire making. One day Johnnie stood back and watched me. Wood being abundant, I had used plenty and had a big, roaring fire with flames leaping skyward. To escape the heat I had stepped back several paces and was sheltering my face with my hat. Johnnie said, "White man heap fool, build heap big fire; burn heap much wood, stand way back, cold. Injun heap smart. Build little fire; little wood, stand close by, warm."

And since I have thought the matter over, I am inclined to believe that Johnnie was right.

Johnnie didn't approve of manual labor. According to his credo, work might be all right for women, white men, and Negroes, but not for him. One day I said, "Johnnie, do you work much?"

"Huh!" said Johnnie. "White man, heap fool, work all time; nigger part fool, work when he have to; Injun, heap smart, no work 'tall."

It had not rained for six weeks, and the snakes were all coming down out of the hills hunting water. Each morning we could see the crooked tracks where they had wriggled across the dusty road on their way to the creek. We were camped on Sallisaw Creek.

One evening between sundown and dusk, we were sitting in camp, talking over the day's happenings. Suddenly one of the men yelled: "There's a copperhead!" Calmly wriggling his way across the open space between our camp chairs was a flat-headed, stub-tailed, mottled-yellow-and-brown reptile, three feet long. Someone grabbed a club and broke its back. The cook, who was afraid of snakes, came with a shovel, gingerly picked it up and started to carry it away. Just as he got to the edge of camp, he let out a shriek fit to wake the dead, jumped four feet into the air, and screamed, "There's another snake." He killed that one with the shovel and carried both snakes into the brush outside the camp. Before he got back, a third copperhead came crawling across the campsite, and before we had killed this one, there came a fourth. We were glad to see the last of "Copperhead Camp" on Sallisaw.

After completing the mapping of Tahlequah Quadrangle, we spent a week in the coal fields of the Choctaw Nation, near Spiro. The party then moved southwestward into the region of the Arbuckles and spent several weeks along the north side of the mountains in the country near Roff, Sulphur, Dougherty, Davis, and old Fort Arbuckle. During the previous summer, Taff and E. O. Ulrich had worked out the geology of the south side of the mountains and had proposed names for the various formations. In ascending order these formations are, Reagan sandstone, Arbuckle limestone, Simpson formation, Viola limestone, Sylvan shale, Hunton formation, Woodford chert, and Sycamore limestone.

Ulrich, a paleontologist of the U. S. Geological Survey, joined the party when we began work in the Arbuckle Mountains and remained with us during the remainder of the season. For many years he has been one of the most eminent geologists in America, and is the recognized authority on certain intricate paleontological problems.

At Sulphur Springs, Chickasaw Nation, there are a number of strong springs from which issue sulphur water. The Secretary of the Interior requested Taff to make an examination of the country. The report on this work was influential in having Platt National Park established by Congress.

From the Arbuckles our party passed westward to the Wichitas in the southwestern part of Oklahoma Territory, and we spent more than a month in preparing a geological map of these mountains. At the time we were in the mountains, the Kiowa and Comanche reservations had just been opened to settlement, and a flood of speculators and mining prospectors had been turned loose in that region.

For many years there had been legends and tales of old Spanish gold mines in the Wichitas. From time to time a few daring prospectors had ventured into the mountains and started sinking shafts in the attempt to discover the treasure or to open up mines, only to be escorted out by the United States Cavalry from Fort Sill.

After the opening of the country to settlement, the bars were down and anyone who wished had the right to stake out a mining claim and prospect for mineral. During the time we were there, August and September, 1901, there were thousands of miners and their families in these mountains. Every little gulch had its mining camp, and the slopes were bristling with claim notices and dotted with shallow mining shafts.

One day I was riding Jinnie-mule across the prairie between two small granite knobs, taking observations with my compass and sketching outcrops for the map, when I saw a pile of fresh dirt and rock a short distance ahead and then something apparently jump up from the ground. I stopped Jinnie and looked again, and could see that a shovelful of dirt was being thrown out. I rode closer and looked down into the hole, where a man was working away with pick and shovel.

107

"Hello, there!" I said. "What's doing?"

"This is a mine, Mister," he replied, looking up at me.

"Oh, a mine," said I. "What kind of a mine?"

"That's all right," said he. "I know what I've got, but I hain't puttin' nothin' out. These guys around here would jump my claim in a minute if they knowed what I've got."

I kept up the conversation, talking about this and that, finally telling him that I was not a miner, but a government man, a geologist, making a map of the mountains. After ten minutes' conversation I must have persuaded him that I was all right, for he began to be more friendly.

"Well," he finally said, "I hain't tellin' any of these fellers what lives around here nothin', but if you're a gov'ment man, I don't mind tellin' you. Mister, I've done struck it rich."

"Indeed!" I replied. "That's fine. Just what kind of mineral have you found?"

"Well, sir," he said, "up to now, I've got gold and silver and copper and a trace of plat'num, an' mighty good prospects for diamonds."

I rode on.

Taff's report on the Wichita Mountains as a possible gold field was unfavorable. Samples had been sent to Washington for analysis and only minute traces of gold and other valuable metals had been found. My observations and conclusions coincided, and in published statements in the *Kansas City Star* and other newspapers I attempted to discourage prospecting. Professor DeBarr, the chemist at the University, as well as several other reputable geologists, chemists, and mineralogists who visited the mountains, found nothing of value and attempted to discourage the useless waste of money in sinking shafts.

These statements aroused the animosity of the miners, many of whom were honest in their belief that there were large amounts of precious metal in the mountains. In their miners' meetings and associations, they passed resolutions condemning and censuring DeBarr, Taff, and me. An article written by miners, speculators, and their friends, that appeared in the public press was intended to discredit us in the minds of the people. Governor Jenkins was petitioned to remove DeBarr and me from the faculty of the University, on the theory that we were using our positions to prevent the development of Oklahoma's resources. Things have long since quieted down, but they were plenty strenuous while they lasted.

There are minerals, plenty and to spare, of various kinds in Oklahoma, but after more than forty years' experience I have yet to be convinced that gold and silver are among them.

It was moving day, and the chief had designated a place near a small creek some ten miles distant for night camp. An hour before sundown the three geologists, Taff, Ulrich, and I rode in, tired and hungry. We found a row in progress. The cook had stopped the camp wagon under a broad elm tree near a spring, unhitched the mules, and started a fire. Before he could get the tent pitched, a big Comanche Indian, on whose allotment the spring was, strode into camp. He was wroth. He said, "Go 'way. No stay here. Me no like um white man. White men burn um wood, muddy um water, horse eat um grass. No like um white men. No camp here. Go."

It looked for awhile as if we would be compelled to move our camp, but the chief of the party, always a diplomat, explained to the Indian that we were government men—Uncle Sam's men —and that we would move on tomorrow.

"You Uncle Sam's men?" said Mr. Buck Indian. "Me like Uncle Sam's men. No like um white men. Stay." So we stayed.

The cook prepared supper. We had fresh meat, beefsteak, that night. We asked our host, Mr. Indian, to be our guest, and we all sat down at the camp table. The Comanche shoved aside his knife, fork and teaspoon, and grabbed the big spoon, trowel fashion, in his right hand, ready for business. We passed him the platter of fried steak. He shook his head. "Meat, my house. This, like um," and he reached for a dish of stewed canned tomatoes and began ladling in with his big spoon. None of the rest of us got a chance at the tomatoes.

My second year at the University of Oklahoma opened favorably. The Legislature had appropriated money for a new main building, specifying that Oklahoma building stone should be used in its construction. The old building was set apart for the sciences, and several rooms were assigned to the use of the Department of Geology.

At that time about the only stone quarry in the Territory was the Armstrong Quarry two miles east of Newkirk. President Boyd asked me to go to Newkirk and inspect the stone in this quarry to see if it was suitable for use in the new building.

I took the train north from Norman, hired a team and driver, and went out to look at the quarry. I soon satisfied myself that the stone was suitable for its intended use. The next train south was not due for several hours, and, as has always been my custom, I began looking around for something of interest in a geological way.

A mile or two off to the southeast I saw a bold hill facing north, overlooking the valley of Arkansas River, and learned that it was Coleman's Bluff. I drove to the foot of the hill and sent the driver down the river road, telling him to take the first road he found west, and to wait for me at the top of the hill. Then I climbed Coleman's Bluff and found myself on a high limestone plateau, some two hundred feet above the level of the river. From this place there is a fine view of the Arkansas River bottoms and the Osage country beyond. On walking south I came to the highest point of the hill, and to my surprise, before me lay an anticline, spread out like a panorama, with the rocks dipping in both directions from the axis, like the roof of a house.

I followed down the anticline for more than a mile, to the road where the driver was waiting, got in the buggy, went back to Newkirk, and took the train for Norman.

In 1902, oil geology was in its infancy and at that time I perhaps did not recognize the importance of the discovery. I suppose I must have told scores of people about this anticline. For several years it was quite a common occurrence for people to say: "Gould, where is there going to be another oil field in Oklahoma?" and my reply was always the same, "Oh, down south of Coleman's Bluff, southeast of Newkirk."

I have since learned by sad experience that information which costs nothing is valued accordingly. At any rate it was nearly ten years before any land was leased in that vicinity.

After I had resigned from state work to practice my profession as consulting geologist, I kept telling people to drill south of Newkirk. At one time some Oklahoma City men with whom I had a contract actually went so far as to secure oil leases on about two thousand acres, covering practically the entire structure. I used to go into their office once or twice a week, and with tears in my voice plead with them to close their options and drill, but they never did so and permitted their leases to expire.

Later, other people leased the land, and the Mervine field, at one time one of the best of the smaller fields of the state, was located on the anticline which I had first seen in 1902. It produced a lot of oil, maybe a million dollars worth, more or less.

During this year, my sister Minnie Rose was enrolled in the University. I had bought a little cottage and we lived together. My second year's teaching at the University was much more satisfactory than the first, because the classes in geology were larger and more interest was being shown in the subject. It was during this winter that I took my first party of students into the Arbuckle Mountains.

The Arbuckles are one of the best places in the United States to study rocks at first hand. In that general region there are all sorts and conditions of geological phenomena. Within a radius of twenty miles, practically every phase of geology, except glacial and volcanic features, may be seen. Rocks of many geological ages, all the way from primitive granite up to coal measures, are exposed. These rocks consist of granite, porphyry, limestone, sandstone, shale, clay, flint, and conglomerate.

Great upheavals of the earth's crust have turned these rocks on edge and folded them into a series of anticlines and synclines. There are many crevices, or faults, where the rocks have slipped up on one side and down on the other side. In crossing the mountains, the Washita River has cut into these various formations, and many of its tributaries are now eating their way back into the rocks, illustrating stream piracy.

These rocks abound in fossils. Scores of genera and species of shells, corals, sponges, and other forms of marine life can be collected. One formation in particular, the Hunton, contains immense numbers of the relics of past life. White Mound, a few miles east of Dougherty, is a famous collecting place. Here a small mound, some twenty feet high, composed of white shale, stands out on the prairie, and its surface is literally covered with small fossils. One might collect for a year on an area not much larger than a city block and still not pick it clean, for each rain washes out more new forms. There are trilobites as large as the end of one's thumb, sponges, corals, mollusks resembling snail shells, and many species of fossil brachiopods.

One evening during the previous summer, when the Survey party was camped at Price's Falls on the north slope of the Arbuckles, the three of us, Taff, Ulrich, and I, were sitting around the campfire talking over the events of the day. We had all been impressed with the unusual geology we had seen. Taff and Ulrich called it Appalachian structure in miniature, or vest-pocket geology, where one might stand on a hill and see spread out before him, like a panorama, a complex series of anticlines and synclines. They agreed that they knew of nothing quite like it in America.

Ulrich turned to me and said, "Gould, you are starting a department of geology in a young university. Here at your back door is a magnificent geological laboratory. You will make a great mistake if you don't bring the young men and women in your classes to the Arbuckle Mountains to learn geology at first hand." To this Taff heartily agreed.

This gave me an inspiration. Starting at Christmas time the same year, 1901, I began taking students in geology into the Arbuckle Mountains. The first year I made the trip, there were only three students, John Hefley, Ralph Sherwin, and Ray Crow. We traveled by wagon from Norman, taking two days for the sixty-mile trip, making night camp near Paoli, and spent several days scouting over the country and picking up fossils. The next year I had four boys who went by train to Dougherty and spent two days in the mountains. The third spring there were about a dozen students, including two girls, my sister and Rose Catlett. We took tents and made camp at a mountain spring.

It was on this third trip, in May, 1903, that the Rock Club, the first geological society of the University of Oklahoma, was organized. It was composed of one instructor and several students. Ralph Sherwin was chairman of the meeting, which was held by the light of a campfire, at a spring near the head of Vines Branch in the hills two miles northwest of Dougherty. Charles T. Kirk was elected president of the club, and Chester A. Reeds, secretary. We adopted a club yell: "Rock Club,

Good Grub, O.U." The name of this society was afterward changed to Pick and Hammer Club. With the organization on the campus of Sigma Gamma Epsilon, it languished and died, but was revived in 1941.

In this humble way began the annual geological trips to the Arbuckle Mountains. The number of students taking the trip gradually increased. Before my connection with the department had ceased, we were making two trips a year, one in the fall and one in the spring. On the autumn trip, camp was usually made at Falls Creek and the students were taken on hikes over the mountains. As the department grew, there were ten to twenty young women and perhaps three times as many men on each trip. Provisions were taken from Norman and also tents enough to house the party in case of rain. Each student took his bedding roll with hammer and collecting bag.

It was the usual practice to leave Norman on the nine o'clock train Wednesday morning, getting into camp about noon. Two or three students who had gone ahead to pitch camp had prepared the first noon lunch. In the afternoon, three parties, each under an instructor, and usually with one or more advanced students who had been on the trip before, tramped five to ten miles over the rocks. By night all parties were back at the camp, supper was prepared and eaten, bonfires were started, and stories, songs, apples, and nuts were enjoyed until nine o'clock, when blankets were spread and everybody turned in. Rising with the first light, our explorers prepared breakfast in a hurry, put noon lunches in collecting bags, and broke into parties to start out again, to be gone until night. Another night camp, and another day's tramp, with a third night in camp, and a half day's walk completed the program. The party took the train at three o'clock Saturday afternoon, which landed us in Norman at six-thirty in the evening. The spring trip was very similar to the one in the fall, except that camp was made at other points and other phenomena were studied.

Many are the students who received their first geological inspiration on these trips. The geologist's laboratory lies out of doors. The chemist, physicist, or zoologist conducts his laboratory within four walls, but the geologist must go into the field and wear out sole leather on the rocks. Many of the early students at the University of Oklahoma who have since made reputations as geologists, teachers or businessmen have told me that the Arbuckle Mountain trip was an eye-opener. They date their first geological zeal to the camping trip in these mountains.

Since my connection with the University has ceased, the trips are still continued. Professor V. E. Monnett, head of the School of Geology, estimates that more than five thousand students have visited these mountains. Not only that, but thousands of students from other colleges and universities in Oklahoma and from institutions in Kansas and Texas have tramped the Arbuckles.

Once I was camping with a party of half a dozen students in the mountains. Our supplies had run low and I came to Dougherty to replenish our stock. At that time there was but one store in town, kept by an immigrant merchant, probably of German origin.

As I stepped into the store, he greeted me: "Vell, mine friend, vot you vant?"

"Two loaves of bread and a pound of bacon," I said.

"Ve dond keep no paked pread for to sell," he replied. "De vimens 'round here all pakes dere own piskits."

"Very well," I said. "How about a small sack of flour?"

"Ve sold de last sack of flour yesterday, and dere vont be no more flour in town till nexd veek," he replied.

"Then I'll take a couple of boxes of crackers," I said. "The boys can make out on crackers for a few days."

"Ve aind got no grackers," he replied. "Dere aind a gracker in dis town. Nobody dond buy 'em here no more. I'll tell you vot, mine friend, in dis town it aind vot you vant, it's vot you can get."

Which, after all, isn't a bad philosophy of life. If one cannot get what he wants, at least he can learn to be content with what he can get.

During the next summer, I had charge of the field party of the Territorial Survey. Professor Van Vleet, who had been in charge in 1901, decided not to take the field this year, and turned the outfit over to me. As assistants, I had Ralph Sherwin and John T. Hefley, who afterward became my brother-in-law. We spent the summer in the western and southwestern parts of the Territory. The object of the trip was to study the gypsum and salt deposits of the area.

There are whole counties in western Oklahoma underlain with gypsum, and in places the drill has penetrated through a solid gypsum ledge for more than one hundred feet. One ledge alone averages ten feet thick and is more than two hundred feet long. As a result of my summer's work, I made the computation that there are, in western Oklahoma, 123,000,000,000 tons of gypsum. There are also seven salt plains, from which a saturated solution of salt brine escapes from springs, and contaminates the streams.

The first scientific publication issued by the University was published by the Oklahoma Territorial Geological and Natural History Survey. It summarized the results of the work of this survey during the field seasons of 1900, 1901, and 1902. One article in this volume dealt with the general geology of the Territory, being the first report on the subject ever published. Another discussed the gypsum deposits. There were also articles by Professor Van Vleet on plants, birds, and snakes of Oklahoma, and a paper entitled "Some Vertebrate Fossils From the

Permian Beds of Oklahoma," by Professor E. C. Case of the University of Michigan.

Fire which broke out in one of my basement rooms on the night of January 6, 1903, totally destroyed the old University building. With it went practically everything that I possessed in the way of scientific equipment. My private library, my instruments, the reprints of papers which I had published, my field notes and lecture notes, more than a hundred boxes of specimens which had never been unpacked, and even my diplomas went up in smoke. Next morning I found myself stripped of all scientific data, except that which my mind contained. It was a matter of starting all over again.

Other departments suffered as much as mine. The next morning President Boyd called the faculty together in a room downtown. Temporary buildings were rented, rooms assigned, and in two days the work of the school was going on almost as usual. For the rest of the year I met my classes in a little room in the second story of an old stone building on west Main Street.

The next year's work at the University was uneventful, except that the classes in geology increased both in number and interest. Some frame buildings had been erected to take the place of the old Science Hall, and a new science building was under construction. My classes being larger, I was beginning to feel the need of an assistant. Minnie Rose spent the year with me, and in the spring received her degree, Bachelor of Arts.

In the spring of 1903, I undertook for the government the investigation of the underground water resources of a portion of the southern part of the Great Plains. The Reclamation Bill, sponsored by President Theodore Roosevelt, had passed Congress the year before, and F. H. Newell had been made director of the Reclamation Service. In order to proceed intelligently with the conservation of the water resources of the West, a vast amount of detailed investigation was necessary. Before reservoirs could be built and irrigation projects established, it was essential to know where water was to be found in sufficient quantity and how it might be best utilized. There were few men in the country who had been trained as water supply experts, and not many of these were in government service. Thus Mr. Newell was obliged to comb the country for men with geological and engineering training to conduct these investigations. That is how I entered the picture.

A telegram from Newell asked me to meet him in Fort Worth to discuss the matter of the investigation of the water resources of Oklahoma and adjacent states. After talking it over with President Boyd, I went to Fort Worth and spent two days arranging details with Newell. He outlined to me what he wished in the way of preliminary work. At that time there was less known regarding the water resources of the southern part of the Great Plains than of almost any other part of the United States. His plan was that for several years I should spend my spare time during summer vacation studying this subject in all its phases and write a series of reports covering the situation. As he expressed it, I was to "cut a swath from Indian Territory to the Rocky Mountains." This I consented to undertake. Mr. Newell instructed me to establish an office at Norman, employ a stenographer and other assistants, and begin the investigation at once. I was to have charge of the work under his general direction, and was given the title of resident hydrographer.

On returning home, I began planning the work. President Boyd gave me a free hand. I opened an office, secured a stenographer, began writing letters to various parts of Oklahoma Territory, trying to secure data on wells, springs and streams. I planned to conduct a field party across western Oklahoma, northeastern New Mexico, and northern Texas during the summer of 1903, making a general reconnaissance of the general

118

region that I was preparing to study in detail. Acting on Newell's suggestion, it was decided that the most feasible plan was to follow up certain streams which cross Oklahoma in order to study the water conditions near the sources.

When the University closed in June, I left Norman with four young men students in the department of geology, Charles T. Kirk, who was afterward state geologist and professor of geology at the University of New Mexico; Chester A. Reeds, later curator of geology at the American Museum of Natural History; Pierce Larkin, now an oil geologist at Tulsa; and Charles A. Long, who for many years has been a missionary in Brazil. We went by train from Norman to Woodward, where we secured an outfit, organized camp, and started westward.

We had a heavy covered wagon with a chuck box on the rear and a team of big mules to haul the camp supplies, also a light spring wagon and saddle horses for rapid reconnaissance, with tents and necessary camp equipment. From Woodward we went west to Beaver County, following up the Cimarron and North Canadian rivers. We camped at Englewood and Liberal, Kansas, and then traveled across the western part of No Man's Land. We were making for Kenton in the Cimarron Valley, near the New Mexico line. In talking with some cowboys at a ranch where we camped one evening, we were told to keep watch next day for a herd of wild horses. Sure enough, in topping a rise on the prairie, we saw the herd grazing on a flat off to our right. On seeing us, they took to their heels and disappeared in a cloud of dust.

As we approached the edge of the plain overlooking the Cimarron Valley from the south, we could see shimmering among the mirages some twenty miles to the northwest what appeared to be a dark-colored hill. As we drew nearer we speculated and wondered what it might be. At one time we decided it must be a row of cedars or pines on the horizon, but still it didn't look quite like trees. Later we decided that it was a flat-topped hill made up of black rocks.

And we were right. We were looking at Black Mesa, but having had no intimation that there was a Black Mesa, or any other kind of mesa, in that part of the world, we were perhaps to be excused for not recognizing it. That night we camped near the little cow town of Kenton on the Cimarron. Next morning, July 4, 1903, we climbed Black Mesa.

The rock is black, volcanic lava, known as basalt. We were to learn later that there are many extinct volcanoes in northeastern New Mexico and southeastern Colorado. A few miles west of Kenton, north of the Cimarron, is an extinct volcanic cone, known as Mesa de Maya. When this volcano was active, great streams of fiery, molten lava belched forth and ran out in great tongues across the plain. The lava stream which extended farthest east transgressed about three miles into what is now Oklahoma before it cooled into basalt. The average width is one-half mile. The thickness of the lava cap at this place is about sixty feet, and the elevation of the flat top is about six hundred feet above the Cimarron.

This is the highest point in Oklahoma, 4,978 feet above sea level. Twenty-five years later, to a day, on July 4, 1928, I took part in a ceremony at Kenton dedicating a monument on top of Black Mesa, the highest point in the state.

From Kenton we traveled up the canyon of the Cimarron to Folsom, New Mexico, and climbed Sierra Grande and Capulin, two extinct volcanic peaks. From Folsom we went up the Cimarron to its head in Johnson Mesa, then crossed over Raton Mesa to Raton. We made a side trip still farther west to the extreme source of the Canadian River just over the state line in southern Colorado. Kirk and I made another side trip and climbed Baldy, one of the highest mountain peaks in New

Mexico, then visited the old mining town, Elizabethtown, then across Morena Valley, through Eagle's Nest Canyon, where Eagle's Nest Lake is now located, and joined the main party at Springer.

The party progressed south along the Canadian River, through Bell Ranch, past Tucumcari, then east across the Panhandle of Texas, where I first caught a glimpse of the dipping beds of dolomite along the Canadian north of Amarillo, and to western Oklahoma. Camp was abandoned at Elk City. The result of this summer's work was published in a government report.

During this summer I was very much in love with a young lady, Nina Swan, who was a student at the University, and who for a time had acted as my stenographer. She was the eldest of the five children of Reverend and Mrs. H. E. Swan. For a number of years, Mr. Swan had been a minister and was then superintendent of the Oklahoma Anti-Saloon League.

With us it was not a case of love at first sight, rather a gradual appreciation of the fact that each was meant for the other, and that life meant nothing unless we could share it together. Friendship ripened into love. We took a buggy ride one evening and settled the matter. The quiet home wedding was at Norman, Friday, September 24, 1903. The officiating minister was J. D. Botkin, my old presiding elder, who had persuaded me to go to Southwestern College. He had also married Mr. and Mrs. Swan. Father and Mother Gould came down from Winfield to attend the ceremony.

We took a short wedding trip to Winfield, came back Sunday, and on Monday I was doing my regular class work. The students were waiting for us, however, and about nine o'clock Monday evening some two hundred of them visited us *en masse*. We had been warned what to expect, so we had plenty of apples and a bushel of roasted peanuts ready for the crowd.

121

They cheered, sang songs, congratulated us, and had a good time for an hour, then went home, and all we had to do was to sweep up the peanut shells.

Two months later, on November 24, 1903, Minnie Rose and John T. Hefley, of Norman, were married at our home. Nina's father, the Reverend H. E. Swan, performed the ceremony.

During the next winter the science departments were again taught in the frame buildings erected after the fire. The new science building, the one still being used at the University, and now known as Old Science Hall, was then in course of construction. Geology was assigned to the top floor, where we were to have plenty of space. The work had grown until an assistant was required, but funds did not permit, and so I still taught all the classes. The first graduate in geology, Charles T. Kirk, received his bachelor's degree in June, 1904.

I had been chosen by the Oklahoma World's Fair Commission to prepare and install an exhibit of Oklahoma minerals for the Louisiana Purchase Exposition at St. Louis, was assigned a small amount of money for the work, and began the preparation of the collection.

It was during this winter that I first attended a meeting of the Geological Society of America, which was held that year in St. Louis. Up to this time I had met very few geologists. Now I saw a hundred or more at one time. My first impression was that geologists were the hairiest bunch of men I had ever seen; most of them wore full beards, but at that time I myself wore a Van Dyke.

The papers, discussions, and lectures given by members of the society were of great interest to me, as was also the banquet given at the Old Southern Hotel by the curators of Shaw's Botanical Gardens. This was the first banquet I ever attended where full-dress was worn and the first where champagne was served.

122

It was at this banquet that I first heard the name Herbert Hoover mentioned. I was seated at a table with two prominent geologists, James F. Kemp of Columbia, and John C. Branner of Stanford. In the course of the conversation Kemp said to Branner, "By the way, John, how is your young man, Hoover, coming on?"

"Hoover," said Branner, with a frown, "Herbert Hoover has given me more trouble than any student I've ever had in the department."

"Why," said Kemp, very much surprised, "I thought young Hoover was a brilliant chap."

"And so he is," replied Branner. "One of the most brilliant young men I've ever known; that's the trouble, he's too brilliant."

"But I don't understand," said Kemp. "How can a young man be too brilliant? I wish we had had him at Columbia."

"Here's the trouble," said Branner. "Bert Hoover graduated in geology at Stanford, has gone out into the business world, and is making a great success as a geologist and mining engineer. He is already a rich man. I would hesitate to say how high that young chap will go. The trouble is that word has got around that Hoover took geology and is getting rich. The result has been that we are now being overwhelmed with mediocrity. It seems almost as though every kid who comes to Stanford these days makes a bee-line for geology, so that we have neither teachers, classroom space, nor laboratories to handle the mob. I sometimes wish that Herbert Hoover had never graduated."

Since that time I have seen the same thing happen many times at other schools. Youngsters with neither the aptitude nor liking for geology have overcrowded classrooms and laboratories, and have added to the teaching load for no other reason than that some former graduate of the department has "made his million in oil." There ought to be a law!

123

During the spring I again went to St. Louis and spent several weeks installing the exhibit. I was there at the time of the formal opening of the exposition and heard Theodore Roosevelt, Grover Cleveland, Cardinal Gibbons, and other noted speakers. After term closed in June my wife and I visited the exposition and remained for two weeks.

In our exhibit we featured building stone and gypsum. The amount of money Oklahoma had to spend for its exhibit was very meager compared to the amount spent by many other states. At that time, neither coal, oil, nor metallic minerals were being produced in Oklahoma Territory, and our only hope was to make a creditable showing with the things we had. I engaged the support of some gypsum-plaster men in Blaine County, who shipped to St. Louis two large blocks of massive white gypsum, each weighing a ton. These blocks I placed on pedestals, so that they stood ten feet above the floor and at the front of the exhibit, where they would catch the eye. During the exposition, I had the pleasure of noting that the Oklahoma booth was usually full of visitors, while many of the more pretentious or spectacular exhibits near by, with plate glass and brass railings, were not so well patronized.

I adopted the policy of sending certain of my geological students from the University to St. Louis in relays every two weeks to look after the exhibits. The commission paid the railroad fare of these students, and their expenses while in St. Louis. By so doing a number of young men who otherwise would not have been able to visit the exposition were permitted to spend a fortnight on the grounds. I met a number of geologists who were in charge of various exhibits and thus was able to extend my geological acquaintance.

I continued my work with the Reclamation Service under Mr. Newell's direction. The department had grown until it was necessary to add an additional man to the teaching force. When

I discussed the matter with President Boyd, it was agreed to secure an assistant, E. G. Woodruff, a graduate in geology from Nebraska. On my recommendation to Mr. Newell, Woodruff was also employed for field work in the Reclamation Service. In July, we left Norman for the eastern part of the Panhandle of Texas. We outfitted at Lawton, Oklahoma, and traveling in a covered wagon, worked westward into Texas, along the head waters of North Fork of Red River, swinging north across Canadian River and as far as Beaver County, then east to the Oklahoma line and south to Mangum. Two and one-half months were spent in the field. The results of the summer's work were afterward embodied in Water Supply Paper 154 of the U. S. Geological Survey, entitled *Geology and Water Resources of the Eastern Portion of the Panhandle of Texas.*

One evening, when the camp was near Shamrock, our neighbor on whose ranch we were camped came down to "set awhile." A tall, dignified Texas gentleman, with a southern drawl, white-bearded and white-haired, one of those men to whom everyone instinctively listens.

We discussed many things, our work, the future of the Panhandle, touched lightly on politics, and then he told us the story of why the cotton boll weevil came to Texas.

"Two years before the first boll weevils found their way across the Rio Grande," he said, "the boys from this county sent me to the legislature. While we were in session at Austin, two government scientists, bug men, came to Austin from Washington, and asked to be permitted to address the session. They told us that the government bug men in Mexico reported that a new kind of injurious insect pest which destroyed cotton was coming our way up along the Gulf Coast. They had kept track of its progress and had found that within a year or two it would reach the Rio Grande at our southern border, and in all probability would cross over and begin to devastate Texas cotton.

125

They said that no way had yet been found to kill off the pest, but that they thought they had devised a plan by which it might be kept from reaching the United States.

"The plan was this: The authorities at Washington suggested that this legislature pass a law prohibiting the raising of cotton in three of the southern counties of Texas, bordering on the Rio Grande and the Gulf of Mexico, and that some plan be worked out to reimburse those few ranchmen in these counties who would suffer from the working of such a law.

"Do you know what that fool legislature did?" said our old friend. "They took a day off and laughed. They hooted the proposition. The very idea of any plug-hatted, stiff-collared dudes from Washington coming down here trying to tell us Texas farmers how to raise cotton! We knew how to raise cotton without any help from Washington or any other place.

"I tried to reason with the boys. I told them that here were some educated men who acted like they knew what they were talking about, who told us that there was a dangerous enemy at our door that was likely to destroy our most valuable crop. These men had suggested a remedy, which was not hard to try, and which might save the state of Texas untold millions of dollars in its cotton crop.

"But it was no use. The boys wouldn't listen. All they would do was laugh. So the government men got mad, packed their grips and went home.

"Two years later, the first boll weevils appeared at Brownsville, and now each year they have been coming farther and farther north. No one knows what the end will be."

This was nearly forty years ago. The boll weevil is still marching on. A conservative estimate of the damage done to the nation's cotton crop by this insect, which but for the thumb-handedness of a fool legislature might have been checked at our southern border, is many hundreds of millions of dollars.

126

As I dropped off to sleep that night I remembered that three thousand years ago the ancient Hebrew prophet Hosea had said, "My people are destroyed for want of knowledge."

The enrollment in the department increased during the winter of 1904–1905. Mr. Woodruff taught mineralogy and physiography, while I carried general geology, paleontology, and economic geology. I also employed several advanced students to assist me in collecting data on the geology of western Oklahoma, preparatory to the publishing of Water Supply Paper 148, entitled *Geology and Water Resources of Oklahoma*. During this winter I attended the meeting of the Geological Society of America at Baltimore and was elected a Fellow of the society. I also became a member of the American Association for the Advancement of Science. In 1905, four men, Chester A. Reeds, Charles A. Long, Harry B. Tosh, and Ellis L. Edwards, graduated in geology.

In the summer of 1905, I again conducted a field party in the Panhandle of Texas. I took with me two advanced students of the department, E. F. Schramm, now head of the Department of Geology at the University of Nebraska, and Tom B. Matthews. We outfitted at Amarillo and spent nearly three months in the western part of the Panhandle working as far north as Beaver County, Oklahoma, and as far west as New Mexico. It was during this year that we explored and prepared a geological map of Palo Duro Canyon, south of Amarillo, giving names to the formations.

We lived off the country, purchasing supplies at the little country stores. On one occasion, when we were working in one of the northwestern counties of the Panhandle, we laid in enough groceries to last two weeks. In those days the government furnished its field parties with a ration list; only certain things might be purchased.

Among other items, we bought at this country store half a

bushel of potatoes. The storekeeper made out his bill for "one half bushel spuds." In making up my accounts at the end of the month, I sent this bill into Washington along with others.

It was disallowed. It appears that the word "spud" was not in the vocabulary of the bright young clerk who passed on all bills sent in from the field. I wrote trying to explain that throughout the Southwest the word "spud" was a perfectly good word, and was universally used for the vegetable, potato, and that what I had bought was a half bushel of potatoes.

The reply was illuminating. It was to the effect that according to the dictionary, which appeared to be the court of last resort, a spud was not a potato but a small spade-like implement used for digging. That spuds were not sold by the half-bushel, that it was inconceivable that one small field party could use that many spuds, and finally that spuds were not on the ration list. Therefore the item was still disallowed.

And so I learned about government red tape. But nevertheless and notwithstanding, I still believe that for forty years Uncle Sam has owed me for one-half a bushel of spuds.

The results of the summer's work were embodied in Water Supply Paper 191, entitled *Geology and Water Resources of the Western Portion of the Panhandle of Texas*. It was on this trip that I first studied the anticlines along the Canadian River which later gave a clue to the location of the Amarillo oil and gas field. I had seen indications of these structures on my first trip across the Panhandle in 1903.

Work was piling up and Woodruff and I decided we needed a student assistant to write labels and lay out specimens. President Boyd assigned us fifteen dollars a month to spend in this way, and we employed a young chap, Everette DeGolyer, to do this work. He was the first student assistant in geology at the University. He has since become wealthy.

CHAPTER 6

I INDULGE IN A PERIPA-
TETIC YEAR AND START A
GEOLOGICAL SURVEY

I HAD BEEN PLAYING a lone hand. My geological ac-
quaintances had not been many, and I knew personally very
few of the men in America who were doing the kind of work
I was attempting to do. My training and experience had all been
in the West. For five years I had been at the University of Oklahoma, doing the best I knew to build up a department and
interest young people in the science of geology, but there was
almost no one in the Territory who "speaks my language." I
wanted to mix with others of my kind and felt that I needed the
inspiration which comes only by personal contact.

On President Boyd's recommendation, I had secured from
the Board of Regents a leave of absence, without pay, for the
academic year of 1905–1906. Ever since receiving my master's
degree from Nebraska, I had been enrolled each year as a graduate student under Professor Barbour's direction, and had been
doing work toward a doctorate.

In September, 1905, I left Oklahoma for Lincoln, where I
enrolled in the university as a candidate for the doctor's degree,
and spent some time on the campus. It was not my intention to
remain at Nebraska for the entire year. My prime object was to
get from the year's work as many things as possible that might

aid me in teaching in Oklahoma. I was especially anxious to learn about those American universities which offered strong courses in geology, and to study at first hand the laboratory and classroom methods there employed. Above all, I wished to come into personal contact with the men who were molding the science of geology in the United States. The only way to do this effectively was to go where those men were working, to travel and observe.

I discussed my ideas with Professor Barbour, who agreed to the plan and gave me all possible encouragement. We both thought that I should not attempt to visit all the large universities in the East, but rather spend some time at each of the eight or ten where noteworthy teaching was being done in geology, and where important research was being carried forward by outstanding men.

I spent some days at the University of Nebraska and made it a point to let as many as possible of the faculty know that I was on the campus. Then I left quietly for St. Louis, where my wife met me. Our daughter, Lois Hazel, was six months old at the time. The name "Lois" was for my Grandmother Gould. "Hazel" was for the color of Nina's eyes.

As we afterward looked back on this year's work, we were never quite able to decide whether we were foolhardy or simply over-ambitious. Perhaps, if it were to have been done over again, we might not have been so venturesome: two young people with a baby and very little ready money to start out on such a trip. But to us it was only a joyous venture, and we were happy and enjoyed every minute of the time.

From St. Louis we went directly to Baltimore, where I enrolled as a graduate student in the Department of Geology at Johns Hopkins University. Here I met Professors Clark, Matthews, Reed, Swartz, and Berry.

It was at Johns Hopkins that I first formed the acquaintance of D. W. Ohern, then a graduate student, who afterwards came to Oklahoma as my successor in the Department and in the Geological Survey. He and I made several trips down the coast of Chesapeake Bay and along the York and Potomac rivers and in Virginia, collecting fossils.

My wife and I found much to interest us in the quaint old city of Baltimore, with its narrow, crooked streets and picturesque buildings, so different from those of the progressive western cities to which we had been accustomed. We took steamboat trips down Chesapeake Bay and visited Washington, where I met a number of men connected with the U. S. Geological Survey.

At Baltimore we lived in a rooming house kept by two old maid sisters from the "Eastern Sho' " who did not seem to know that the Civil War was over. One of the young lady boarders asked if we were acquainted with a friend of hers who lived in Butte, Montana. When I tried to explain that it was farther from Norman, Oklahoma, to Butte than from Norman to Baltimore, she became very indignant. From her I learned something of the total ignorance of the average Easterner regarding that part of the United States that lies west of the Allegheny Mountains.

While at Johns Hopkins I enrolled in courses with Clark, Swartz, and Reed, but did not remain in the university until the end of the semester. A good part of my time, while in Baltimore, was spent in the geological laboratories and in the library, trying to become better acquainted with geological literature.

In December, we left Baltimore for New York City, where we spent a few days sightseeing. I visited Columbia University attending the classes of Professors Kemp, Berkey, and Grabau. Considerable time was spent in the museums at Columbia, the American Museum of Natural History, and the Metropolitan Art Museum.

Holidays were approaching and we left New York for Fitchburg, Massachusetts, where we visited a cousin whom I had not seen since early childhood. My wife and daughter remained at Fitchburg while I went to Ottawa, Canada, to attend the meeting of the Geological Society of America. There I met or renewed acquaintance with a number of leading geologists, especially the Canadians.

At Ottawa the snow was deep on the ground, and travel on the streets was chiefly by sleds. This was before the time of automobiles, and horse-drawn vehicles carried the traffic. All the delivery wagons and milk wagons were on runners, but the thing that impressed me most was that the baby carriages were on tiny sleds.

We next visited Harvard, remaining two weeks at Cambridge and Boston. I was especially interested in the Agassiz Museum, and in the methods of instruction employed by Professors Woodward and Shaler. Professor Shaler was at that time the dean of American geologists, an old man and quite feeble, but one whose interest in science never lagged. It has been said that, during his time, more young men came under his personal instruction than under any other teacher in America. For many years his courses in geology were exceedingly popular among the Harvard students, and his classes usually numbered hundreds. After sitting in his recitation room, I could appreciate why this must be so. His lectures were veritable romances into which he skillfully wove scientific facts with glowing word pictures in an inimitable manner.

It was at Harvard that I heard a story concerning two very noted American scientists, Louis Agassiz and Nathaniel S. Shaler. Agassiz had been teaching all the natural science at Harvard for several years, and as the teaching load became too heavy, a young Kentuckian named Shaler had been secured to take over geology. When he arrived on the campus, Shaler had with him an elaborate series of notes for use in the classroom.

Being rather proud of them, he handed the notes to Agassiz for comment and suggestion.

Agassiz took the notes but did not return them. As the day for the opening of term approached, Shaler became uneasy, and finally, just before time to go to his first class, he asked Agassiz for his notes.

"Dose notes," said Agassiz, "Oh, I purn dose notes. If you got it in your head vot you vant of notes?"

And so Shaler had to appear before his first class and lecture extemporaneously. The story goes that never after did he use notes in the classroom.

At Harvard I first met William Morris Davis, who was perhaps the outstanding American geographer. A dignified gentleman, shrewd and cultured, he had written a number of books on geography and physiography.

But at a meeting of the Geological Society of America some years later, I saw him lose his temper. Davis was a short, portly, bald-headed man who wore chin whiskers. At a smoker, some of the more frolicsome of the geologists were improvising rhymes, taking off the idiosyncrasies and peculiarities of the various men. Someone chimed in with the following couplet:

D is for Davis with peneplaned crest,
His chin is prograded, and also his vest.

It should be explained that "peneplaned" and "prograded" were two of Davis's pet terms. Anyhow, he didn't appreciate the poetry. He sputtered.

Yale University, where the great James D. Dana had lived and worked, was our next stop. I examined the noted collections of vertebrate fossils secured by O. C. Marsh, and visited the mineralogical laboratories of Brush and Penfield. I also renewed my acquaintance with Professor Schuchert, one of the great paleontologists in America.

Schuchert had been a poor boy who had never gone to college a day in his life. He had a natural liking for fossils and by sheer force of personality forged his way to the top. He had written a number of textbooks on historical geology which have been studied by thousands of young men and women throughout the world.

At Yale I also met H. E. Gregory, Isaiah Bowman, and other members of the geological faculty. At that time, Chester A. Reeds, one of my former students, was taking graduate work in paleontology under Schuchert. He later received his doctor's degree and taught geology for three years in Bryn Mawr College before going to New York, where for many years he was curator of geology in the American Museum of Natural History.

On leaving Yale, we spent a week at Cornell University, "far above Cayuga's waters," at Ithaca, New York. At this time my old Winfield College friend, Paul J. White, was taking postgraduate work in the Department of Agriculture at Cornell. Here I met Professors Tarr, Ries, and Harris.

From Cornell we started west, visiting Niagara Falls en route to the University of Michigan. I was especially anxious to visit the classrooms of Professor Israel C. Russell, who had been teaching geology at this university for many years. Russell was an old man with long white whiskers, quite feeble. He died within a year after my visit. He was a profound scholar, a traveler of renown, and a writer of interesting books. Many of us think that his series including *Rivers of North America* and *Lakes of North America* has never been excelled. At Michigan I also met Frank Leverett, one of our leading glaciologists.

The University of Chicago was next on our itinerary. At that time several of the strongest men in American geology were teaching there. T. C. Chamberlin, who at the time stood at the head of American geologists, was chairman of the department. Associated with him was R. D. Salisbury, who was considered by many persons to be one of the best teachers in any American university. Salisbury was to Chicago what, some years earlier, Shaler had been to Harvard, a man whose methods of instruction were so outstanding that students flocked to his classes. My old friend and adviser, Professor Williston, was at the head of the Department of Paleontology, and at that time was devoting his research to Permian vertebrates, while Stewart Weller taught invertebrate paleontology and stratigraphy.

I left my wife and baby girl at Chicago for a few days and ran up to Madison, Wisconsin, in order to visit the university, where I met, among others, the trio of outstanding men, Leith, Fenneman, and Blackwelder. Professor Van Hise, who was numbered among the half dozen leading geologists in America, was president of the university and busy with executive work.

At each of these eight universities, I learned certain things about teaching geology. I learned the methods used, the results obtained, and more than all else, I learned the personalities of the men. These men differed greatly, one from the other. Some like Shaler, Salisbury, Davis, Swartz and Kemp, were outstanding teachers, while others like Schuchert, Grabau, Harris, Williston, and Berry were primarily research men, but each man had outstanding traits that endeared him to his students and to his associates. And these men, specialists in various branches of the science in which we were mutually interested, were most kind to the self-made country boy who was content to sit at their feet and learn.

And such different associations and environment! Here were old, ivy-clad buildings, ripened by time and mellowed by tradition, with shady walks and dignified surroundings. Here were men steeped in the lore of science, surrounded by the best culture of America; men whose heritage had taught them the ways of living, to whom these things were part of their daily life, to whom education and culture were as natural as breathing.

How different from the raw, unformed institution with which my lot had been cast. I used to wonder if Oklahoma would ever reach the place where it could successfully compete with the older schools. I am thankful that I have lived to see the day when our University has taken its place among the foremost institutions in the land.

From Chicago, we left for the University of Nebraska, arriving in March. I immediately took up again the study of the fossil leaves upon which I had been engaged during the winter of 1899–1900, and which ever since that time had been stored in the basement. Nina aided me in the preparation of a report on these leaves, in which I named and described a number of new species. I believe that this report has never been published.

While little Lois played in the room, Nina clicked the typewriter and I revised manuscript, and pored over French, in which, much to my disgust, I was compelled to take an examination.

The work was strenuous, but by applying ourselves almost day and night for several weeks, we were able to complete it on time. The faculty was kind enough to accept my report, Water Supply Paper Number 148, entitled *Geology and Water Resources of Oklahoma,* in lieu of a doctor's dissertation. I had no difficulty in passing the oral examination, and at commencement time, 1906, received the degree of Doctor of Philosophy, for which I had striven so long.

Taking everything into account, I have always considered this peripatetic year spent in visiting eastern universities and completing the work for my doctorate, to be the most profitable I have ever spent. The acquaintanceships which I formed have since stood me in good stead. The insight that I acquired into methods of other teachers aided me greatly in my class-room work.

Mr. Woodruff had charge of the department during my absence, and five men graduated this year, E. F. Schramm, Tom B. Matthews, Ira Montgomery, W. H. Low, and H. A. Everest. On returning from Nebraska in June, I immediately took charge of a field party for the Territorial Survey. Professor Van Vleet had conducted several parties during the few years immediately preceding, while I was engaged in government work, and he wished me to take over during this summer. It was the last time that this Survey ever had a party in the field.

Two advanced students in geology, L. L. Hutchison and R. R. Severin, accompanied me. The work was in eastern Oklahoma Territory and the northern part of Indian Territory. The object was to conduct a reconnaissance, looking into the oil fields and coal deposits of the region. We outfitted in Pawnee County, worked east through the Cleveland oil field, the only one in Oklahoma Territory at that time, crossed into the Osage country, to Pawhuska, thence east to Bartlesville, examining the Bartlesville, Nowata, and Chelsea oil fields, then south to Muskogee and west through Morris, Okmulgee, and Tulsa, and back to Pawnee. During the summer we visited practically all the oil fields that had been developed in Indian Territory.

During the winter of 1906–1907, I again took up teaching at the University. Woodruff was granted a leave of absence to do graduate work. At the close of this year he did not return, but took a permanent position with the U. S. Geological Survey.

My assistant this year was Frank F. Grout, a graduate of Minnesota. Before the end of the year he accepted an offer to teach mineralogy in his *alma mater*. L. L. Hutchison and R. R. Severin graduated in geology. I completed my work on Water Supply Paper Number 191, entitled *Geology and Water Supply of the Western Portion of the Panhandle of Texas*, the last of the three reports on the water resources of the Great Plains which I had been writing for the U. S. Geological Survey. I attended a session of the American Mining Congress at Joplin, Missouri, acting as secretary of the committee on resolutions, and was elected the Oklahoma vice president for this congress.

I was engaged in private work in the oil fields during the summer of 1907. Oil development was beginning to be active, and a few of the more progressive operators were learning that the geologists might be of some benefit in the location of prospective oil fields. I was employed by a company actively engaged in the development of oil properties, and spent the entire summer in the endeavor to locate prospective oil fields. The greater part of the work was in the vicinity of Muskogee, Coweta, and Chelsea.

The Oklahoma Constitutional Convention was held in 1906. For many years there had been much agitation looking toward the admission of Oklahoma to the Union, for it had grown rapidly in both wealth and population. Congress had delayed year after year until the people were becoming thoroughly impatient and disgusted with its dilatory measures. Many of the best citizens favored the formation of two states, one to be composed of Oklahoma Territory and the other of Indian Territory. The history of these two political subdivisions has been written many times. I can here do no more than sketch it briefly.

All of the present state of Oklahoma, except the three northwestern counties, formerly known as "No Man's Land" or the "Neutral Strip," and now spoken of as the "Panhandle of Oklahoma," originally belonged to the Five Civilized Tribes, that is, the Cherokees, Creeks, Choctaws, Chickasaws, and Seminoles. These Indians once lived in the southern states east of the Mississippi River, where, during the early part of the nineteenth century, they had attained a comparatively high state of civilization. Their land was sought by the white man, and, beginning about 1830, various treaties were entered into with the different tribes, whereby these people relinquished their lands in the southern states and received in lieu thereof certain lands in what is now Oklahoma. During two decades between 1830 and 1850, many members of these various tribes migrated westward and settled in their new homes.

During the Civil War these nations threw their fortunes with the Confederacy, and at the close of the war the federal authorities forced them to make treaties whereby the western part of their domain was ceded back to the central government.

Beginning about 1870, the United States government inaugurated the policy of settling in this western portion of the Indian Territory various tribes, and scattered remnants of tribes, from all parts of the United States. Among those which were brought in were the Pawnees, Otoes, and Missouris from Nebraska, the Kaws and Osages from Kansas, and the Iowas, Potawatomis, Shawnees, Kickapoos, Tonkawas, and Sacs and Foxes, from various parts of the country. The "wild Indians of the Plains," namely the Kiowas, Comanches, Cheyennes, Arapahoes, Apaches, and others, were settled on reservations in the western part of this region.

After this territory had been assigned to the various Indian tribes, there still remained, near the central part of the region, an area of about 2,700 square miles which had not been assigned to any Indian tribe. This became known as the "Unassigned Lands" or the "Oklahoma Country." The word Oklahoma is derived from two Choctaw words, *okla*, meaning people, and *homa*, meaning red. During the late seventies and eighties many persons, acting on the theory that it was government land and open to homestead entry, attempted to settle upon this unassigned land. They were not permitted to remain but were driven off by United States troops.

Many "boomer" colonies, headed by such brave spirits as

David L. Payne and W. L. Couch, made pilgrimages from Kansas into this land of promise but were forced out by the troops. On April 22, 1889, the land was finally opened to settlement. Prospective settlers gathered on the border of the territory, and, at the crack of the pistol at noon, started on a mad race for claims, which has since been known as "the Run." Those who slipped in the night before and secured the best claims were known as "Sooners." Practically the entire territory was settled the first day. Cities sprang up as by magic, and soon thereafter a territorial government was established.

At different times, treaties were made with the Indian tribes that had been brought in and settled in the region surrounding the Oklahoma Country, and one by one the lands of these various peoples were thrown open to settlement, until by the year 1901, practically all the Oklahoma country had been settled by whites.

Conditions in the country belonging to the Five Civilized Tribes were very different. Here the Indians owned all the land (usually in Common) and steadfastly refused to give it up. Finally Congress appointed a commission, known as the Commission to the Five Civilized Tribes, but usually spoken of as the Dawes Commission, which spent a number of years in settlement of the affairs of these five tribes. The land was surveyed and appraised and allotted to the individual Indian citizens. Each man, woman and child belonging to the Five Civilized Tribes received his quota of land.

When this had been accomplished, Congress passed an Enabling Act permitting the citizens of the two territories (Oklahoma and Indian) to call a constitutional convention and to prepare a constitution for the new state of Oklahoma. This convention met in the fall of 1906, at Guthrie, the capital of Oklahoma Territory, and remained in session several months, during which the state constitution was written.

I long had in mind the establishment of a geological survey in the new state. I knew personally a number of the members of the Constitutional Convention. Professor James S. Buchanan, head of the History Department in the University of Oklahoma, represented Cleveland County. Because of my acquaintance in the two territories, I had little difficulty in having appointed a committee on a geological survey. The chairman of this committee was W. J. Caudill of Hobart. Professor Buchanan was a member, and others were J. J. Sorrels, of Milton; J. B. Curl, of Bartlesville, and Boone Williams of Lehigh. I met with the committee several times and aided them in formulating plans for the establishment of a survey. The provision recommended by this committee passed the convention and was written into the Constitution. It is contained in Section 37 of Article 5 of the Constitution of Oklahoma, which reads: "The legislature shall provide for the establishment of a State Geological and Economic Survey." Oklahoma is the only state in the Union possessing a constitutional warrant for the establishment of a geological survey.

During the time that the Constitutional Convention was in session, I was busy with school work. Chester A. Reeds, who taught mineralogy this year, was of great assistance in looking after my classes while I was busy at Guthrie.

Our son, Donald Boyd, was born on December 6, 1906. I remember that Mr. Caudill was very much elated when I announced this fact, and when he called the committee together, the men all congratulated me on the birth of a son and decided we would have to call the boy the Geological Survey baby.

As soon as the Constitution had been adopted, I began work on the formulation of a law providing for carrying out the plans I had in mind for so many years. I wrote to the various state surveys, and even to Australia and Canada, to obtain copies of the laws under which the various surveys operated.

After studying these laws and securing the opinion of a number of state geologists, I drafted the bill vitalizing the constitutional provision and establishing the survey. My object was to have the law concise, and at the same time flexible. I did not wish to burden it with too many provisions, but on the other hand I endeavored to foresee all possible emergencies. I wished to avoid the danger of a large governing board, knowing the difficulty of securing a quorum for the transaction of business, while, on the other hand, I did not wish to leave the appointment of the state geologist to any one individual, not even the governor of the state, knowing that in this case partisan politics and inefficiency were apt to creep in.

As finally written, the law provided for the establishment of a Geological Survey Commission consisting of the governor, the state superintendent of public instruction, and the president of the University of Oklahoma. These three men were to appoint as director of the survey a geologist of established reputation. He in turn appointed his assistants. The law contains but nine sections and is so worded that, under its provisions, the state geologist can do almost anything he desires.

After having settled in my own mind the kind of law I wanted, the next thing was to get the law on the statute books. Again my acquaintance over the state stood me in good stead. I knew personally nearly half the members of the first State Legislature and constituents of several other members. The bill, as I had written it, was introduced into the Senate by Senator Roy Stafford of Oklahoma City, editor of the *Daily Oklahoman,* and Senator Sorrels of Milton. As first written, it provided for an appropriation of ten thousand dollars for the first year, but when discussing it in committee, Senator Stafford suggested that the amount be raised to fifteen thousand dollars, which was done. This is probably the only case on record where one got more from a legislature than he asked for. There was little opposition to the bill, either in the House or in the Senate, and it passed as written and was approved by Governor Haskell, May 29, 1908.

Times were strenuous in Oklahoma that year. Charles N. Haskell, the first governor of the state, a very shrewd politician and far-sighted man, was having his own troubles. His political enemies, both in and out of his own party, were bombarding him from all sides, and he was busy day and night. I made several attempts to get the Governor's ear in order that he might call together the Geological Survey Commission, but it was not until late in July of that year that the organization was finally effected.

I remember the circumstances very well. The Governor and I were both on a train en route to Muskogee, where the Southern Commercial Congress was holding its annual meeting. Governor Haskell was scheduled to address the congress on the subject "The State of Oklahoma." All the way from Guthrie we sat in the same car, but after a casual word or two when he first saw me, we had no chance for conversation. He was constantly surrounded by friends and politicians, and although I was very anxious to have a word with him, I did not care to interrupt. Half an hour before the train reached Muskogee, he excused himself from his party, walked over to my seat and sat down.

His first question was: "Gould, what do you know about the minerals of Oklahoma?"

That was my opportunity. I started in, and for ten minutes gave him facts and figures about the mineral resources of the state. Other friends came up and interrupted him, but on parting he said:

"Can you be at my office next Monday at nine o'clock?"

I told him I could be there.

"We will have President Evans up," he said, "and will organize the Geological Survey." Even then he gave no intimation of the fact that he had me in mind for director.

That afternoon Governor Haskell addressed the Southern Commercial Congress, speaking for more than an hour on the resources of Oklahoma, and during half of that time he discussed Oklahoma's mineral resources, but he said very little that I had not told him in my ten-minute talk. But he said it much better than I could have done. This was one of Governor Haskell's strong points; his unusual ability to take facts, figures, and statements from those whom he met, dress them up in his own picturesque and vivid language, and impress them upon his hearers. Charles N. Haskell was one of the most versatile and resourceful public men with whom I ever came in contact.

Acting on Governor Haskell's request, I was in his office at nine o'clock on Monday, July 25, 1908. President Evans and State Superintendent Cameron were present. In order to avoid interruption, Governor Haskell took the members of the Geological Survey Commission, with myself and a stenographer, and adjourned to the office of the lieutenant governor. Governor Haskell called the commission to order. The Governor was elected chairman, the State Superintendent, secretary, and the President of the University was elected executive officer of the commission. President Evans presented my name for the directorship of the survey, and I was elected. I had prepared, in the form of a resolution, instructions, or a general working plan, for the operation of the survey. I handed this resolution to the secretary and it was adopted by the commission as follows:

"The Director of the Oklahoma Geological Survey is instructed:

"To proceed to ascertain the relations existing between the different rock formations at or near the surface of the earth in Oklahoma and to prepare reports properly illustrated, setting forth these facts.

"To examine as rapidly as possible, the various mineral resources of the State and prepare reports outlining their distribution.

"To collect, name, and arrange a collection of specimens illustrating the geology and mineral resources of the State.

"To assist the colleges and high schools in making collections of geological and mineralogical specimens.

"To disseminate, as widely as possible, particularly by correspondence and public addresses, correct ideas as to the occurrence, origin, and relation of rocks, minerals and ores.

"To answer all reasonable inquiries relative to the mineral resources of the State.

"To examine, upon petition of fifty freeholders, properly certified by the county clerk, land upon which valuable mineral resources may be thought to exist.

"To analyze free of cost, such specimens as, in the opinion of the director, may be thought to contain valuable minerals or which would further the work of the survey.

"To prepare a schedule of prices to be charged by the chemist of the survey for analysis made of such material as is not analyzed on the authority of the director.

"To cooperate with the United States Geological Survey, other bureaus of the United States Government and other state surveys, whenever benefit would accrue to the State."

These instructions have since served as the constitution of the Oklahoma Geological Survey.

The director of the Geological Survey was also given special instructions to guide him during the current year.

"Begin immediately to investigate location and accessibility of various building stones of the State, including limestone, marble, sandstone, granite, gabbro, gypsum, dolomite, and porphyry, with tests to determine the availability of this stone for the construction of public buildings.

145

"Begin immediately to investigate the location and availability of all stone, clay, and other minerals of the State, suitable for the construction of roads, with ample tests to determine the relative value of the different materials in the construction of roads.

"Begin immediately to investigate as fully as possible the oil and gas fields of Oklahoma. Also to prepare and present to the commission reports fully illustrated setting forth the facts relating to these subjects."

And that is how it happened.

CHAPTER 7

STATE GEOLOGIST OF OKLAHOMA

THE FIRST of my three self-imposed tasks had been accomplished. I had organized and been head of a department of geology in a state university and had nursed it through its early years. The department was already turning out graduates who were destined to make names for themselves and bring honor to their *alma mater.*

I had spent a year in the East becoming acquainted with many of the leading geologists of America and had acquired my doctorate. I was now ready to tackle my second objective, to serve as state geologist.

Having had an inkling of what was to be done at the meeting of the commission in Guthrie, I had made tentative arrangements for the rapid organization of field parties. The season was already well advanced and speed essential. Within an hour after my appointment I had long distance telephone calls to five men in different parts of Oklahoma, directing them to begin field work. During the remainder of the summer nine different parties were in the field.

I appointed L. L. Hutchison as assistant director of the survey, and assigned to him Ben C. Belt, Artie C. Reeds, W. J. Cross, and T. R. Corr. Hutchison's party spent the remainder of the season in Tulsa, Creek, Okmulgee, Muskogee, and Wagoner counties, investigating the oil and gas fields. A second party was organized at Ponca City and placed in temporary

147

charge of H. A. Everest. Everett Carpenter and H. G. Powell accompanied him and worked across the northern part of the oil fields, chiefly in Osage, Washington, and Nowata counties. Pierce Larkin was assigned to investigate the Cretaceous area of southern Oklahoma. He worked from Ardmore past Atoka and Durant to the Arkansas line. Chester A. Reeds spent the season in the Arbuckle Mountains. Frank A. Herald and Chester C. Clark spent several weeks studying the gypsum and salt formations in the western part of the state. G. W. Kneisly undertook the examination of the granite rocks in the Wichita and Arbuckle mountains. Gaylord Nelson was assigned to work on the Portland cement beds in eastern Oklahoma. He visited a number of limestone quarries and made a study of the various geological formations from which Portland cement might be manufactured. Key Wolf spent several weeks in the southeastern counties tracing out the Wapanucka limestone.

The work of the summer was satisfactory and I felt that the results accomplished justified the expenditure of the money, in spite of the fact that the men were not thoroughly trained and the parties were not able to get into the field until nearly the first of August. The work necessarily closed with the opening of school in September.

It was during this summer that D. W. Ohern first came to Oklahoma. We had met at Johns Hopkins in the fall of 1905. He was my choice of the men available for the work in the University of Oklahoma. A western man with eastern training, a graduate of Drake University and of the University of West Virginia, he had received his doctor's degree from Johns Hopkins. It was understood that in case I became state geologist I was to retain my position as head of the department, but that I was to be relieved of teaching. I wired Ohern, asking him if he would come to Oklahoma and take the position in the department of geology and also take charge of a field party for the survey. He came to Oklahoma and joined the party which had been in temporary charge of Mr. Everest, and spent the remainder of the summer in the oil fields of northern Oklahoma.

According to the law establishing a survey, it was provided that until suitable laboratories, office rooms, libraries, etc., had been provided by the state, the University should furnish rooms and equipment, but there were no University rooms available. The new Administration Building at the University had burned December 20, 1906, this being the second disastrous fire within a four-year period. After this fire, all the departments were crowded into the buildings then on the campus, which were by no means adequate to do the work at hand. I rented four rooms near my home and installed the offices of the survey. As chemist I employed L. C. Snider, a graduate of the University of Indiana and a former student of J. W. Beede. As draftsman I secured Frank Gahrtz from the Missouri Survey.

During the following winter I was very busy trying to get into type some reports on the general geology and oil resources of the state. The people were beginning to look to the survey for information and many requests were coming in for reports on various subjects. A considerable part of my time was spent in traveling over Oklahoma investigating the minerals of various regions, lecturing, and writing letters on subjects dealing with the mineral resources of the state.

On one occasion I had taken the train to Watonga to examine a reported copper deposit in the Gypsum Hills northeast of town. Hiring a team and buggy at a livery stable, I drove to the property, made my inspection, but found no copper, and started back. Crossing a ditch in the road, the buggy slipped and smashed a wheel. I walked half a mile to a homesteader's shack, borrowed an ax, cut a pole to hold up the rear axle, and managed to cripple my way back to town.

The owner of the livery outfit was not pleased. We had quite an acrimonious debate as to who should pay for the wheel. Finally we compromised. I gave him four dollars, which was nearly all the money I had with me.

It was late in the afternoon and I had eaten nothing since leaving Norman at daylight. I had a return ticket to Norman, a healthy appetite, and a nickel. The train was due in half an hour.

I went into a hole-in-the-wall eating-house near the depot and parked myself on a stool at the counter near a bottle of tomato ketchup. The proprietor came out of the back room.

"What ye want?" he said.

I threw the nickel on the counter and said, "That's all the money I've got. Will it buy a bowl of hot water, a pat of butter and a bowl of crackers?"

He looked at me and then at the nickel a moment, and said, "Yep, guess that's about right."

He went back to the kitchen and brought out the bowl of hot water, dipped up some crackers from a barrel, fished out a pat of butter, set them on the counter, and went away.

I reached for the ketchup bottle and bankrupted it into the hot water, seasoned it with butter, salt and pepper, dumped in the crackers, and had a supper to fill a hungry geologist.

In November, 1908, Bulletin Number 1 of the Oklahoma Geological Survey entitled *Preliminary Report on the Mineral Resources of Oklahoma* was published.

The work of the department increased. Professor Ohern proved to be a most interesting and inspiring lecturer, a teacher whom students liked. He developed into a good faculty man and was appointed on a number of important committees. Pierce Larkin was his assistant.

The second legislature was about to meet, and I prepared a bill providing funds for the survey expenses for the coming biennium. This bill carried an appropriation of seventeen thousand dollars a year for the two years. By a stenographic mistake somewhere along the line in committee, the bill was made to include the following items: "Special investigations for gold, silver, copper, lead, zinc, and other minerals, $4,000 per annum." This was very different from the wording of the clause when I sent it to the committee. My intention was to have four thousand dollars available for general field work, particularly on oil, gas, coal and building materials. The bill passed both the Senate and the House, but the clause carrying the four thousand dollars per year appropriation for investigations on gold, silver, etc., was disapproved by Governor Haskell. The cutting of this amount sadly handicapped the survey in the matter of field work for the following two years. We were obliged to abandon a considerable amount of investigations which had been planned.

Two field parties were sent out during the summer of 1909. Professor Ohern worked through the oil fields in the northeastern part of the state. With him were Everett Carpenter, Frank Herald, Key Wolf, Artie Reeds, W. J. Hazeltine, Robert H. Wood, and Ben C. Belt. All these men except Wolf have since become prominent geologists. Hutchison spent the greater part of the summer in southern Oklahoma investigating the asphalt deposits.

Charles H. Taylor came to the University in the fall of 1909. He had specialized in mineralogy and economic geology at the University of Chicago and was well qualified to take up this phase of the work while Professor Ohern retained the general geology and paleontology.

There was great turmoil at the University during the winter and spring of 1908. For the first time partisan politics began to play an important factor in school matters throughout Oklahoma.

The first Territorial Legislature of Oklahoma, which met at Guthrie in 1890, established three state schools, the University at Norman, the Agricultural and Mechanical College at Stillwater, and the normal school at Edmond. David Ross Boyd was made president of the University and retained that position for seventeen years, or until after statehood.

Conditions at the University had always been harmonious. President Boyd was a capable and efficient institutional executive and had surrounded himself with a faculty of specialists, men who knew their subjects well. In trying out a new man at the University, there had been but one standard—efficiency. Nothing concerned with church affiliations, political influence, or any other consideration mattered. If a man was a good teacher and could attract students, he remained on the faculty. If not, President Boyd saw to it that his place was given to another.

With the advent of statehood, conditions changed. The University Board of Regents appointed by the new Governor consisted largely of politicians. The most active member of the board, and the one who soon proved himself to be the most skillful manipulator, was a preacher who made politics his business. At the first meeting of the new board, eight men, including President Boyd, were dismissed. These were men who had been with the University for several years and who had proved their ability and worth. Nineteen new members were elected to the faculty, including three members of one family, a father, daughter, and nephew. The presidency was given to the Reverend A. Grant Evans, a personal friend of the Governor.

Let me cite a case which came under my personal observation. In territorial days, a minister came to Oklahoma from an eastern state. He was an educated man, a classical scholar, who read Latin, Greek, and Hebrew, and was schooled in logic and philosophy. For many years he served his church well and faithfully, and was rewarded by being given a teaching position in a college established by this church. This was the time, which some of us remember, when denominational colleges were springing up all over Oklahoma and Indian Territory. The story of the rise and fall of these schools, and their struggles for existence before giving up the ghost, is still in the ink pot; perhaps some day a future historian will record it.

For several years our friend occupied the chair of ancient languages and philosophy at this small college. Finally the school winked out and he was left without a job. In the first general election after statehood, he seems to have interested himself in politics and made speeches in favor of certain candidates. As a reward for services rendered, it is said, he was promised a job as teacher in one of the state schools. After statehood, he sent to the state superintendent a list of subjects that he preferred to teach. He listed three choices, first, ancient languages; second, philosophy; and third, mathematics. The newly appointed Board of Regents met, the state superintendent being a member. Our minister friend was elected to teach geography and geology in a state normal school.

Imagine the situation! Here was a man well along in years whose training had been largely in classics, elected to a faculty to try to teach young Oklahomans something about how their state had been stuck together, and what its resources and potentialities were. I doubt if in all his life he had read ten pages of geology. Not only that, but his training, his heritage, his experience, and his thinking had been foreign, if not antagonistic, to geological thought. To him a rock was simply a rock, but whether sandstone, limestone, or granite, he did not know or care. He could not even recognize volcanic lava, and during the first year of his teaching he actually identified as a volcanic rock a bit of ferruginous sandstone found in the Oklahoma red beds. Under these circumstances, what was a man to do?

The first thing he did was to come to Norman, where I had been teaching geology, and present his case. I sensed his predicament and did everything in my power to help. I lent him books to read, recommended geological texts, tried to give him some slight knowledge of the geology and resources of the new state of Oklahoma. I even found a place for him in one of the field parties which I was sending out.

Rarely have I seen a man more appreciative. He was a high-class, a sweet-spirited individual, and I came to respect him very highly. He tried earnestly to readjust his thinking and to adopt new viewpoints, not an easy thing for any of us to do, especially for a man past middle life.

On the opening of the school, he started his classes. All he could do was to read ahead of his pupils and try to teach the textbook. After a short time he was shifted to instruct in reading. The last I heard of him, he had given up the attempt to teach and was living on a small farm.

President Evans, on assuming charge of the University of Oklahoma, attempted to revise much of the policy. He was handicapped on all sides throughout his entire administration. The places of the efficient men who had been dismissed by the board were filled with men unadjusted to new situations. President Evans's training and experience had been that of a missionary to the Cherokee Indians and president of a struggling denominational college in Indian Territory. After three years, he was retired and Julien C. Monnet, dean of the College of Law, was made acting president for one year until the election of Stratton D. Brooks.

Personally, my relations with President Evans were always very satisfactory. He turned the work of the survey over to me, signed vouchers when I laid them on his desk, warmly seconded me in all matters, and was in every way genial, kindly, and pleasant, so that I learned to admire him very much.

The work of the survey occupied all my time and I was not able to look after the details of the department. Professor Ohern, however, had proved more than equal to this task, and on my recommendation he was made head of the Department of Geology. I retained a position on the faculty with the title "Professor of Oklahoma Geology" until the time of my resignation from state work. During the three years I had charge of the state survey, Professor Ohern built up the department in a most creditable way.

Even before assuming my duties as state geologist, I had found that people in many parts of the state were anxious for special examinations of many regions, looking toward the development of various mineral resources. I began to receive letters from men who were interested in some particular mineral product, calling for examinations.

Perhaps the man who sent the request imagined he had gold, which turned out to be iron pyrite, or possibly an oil field, or a rock which he thought might make Portland cement. I soon found that it would be impossible to satisfy even a small part of these requests. The problem was solved by sending out a blank form of petition to be signed by fifty taxpayers of the county and certified by the county clerk, requesting that an examination be made of a certain property or of a definite region. I emphasized the fact that the survey had no desire to engage in the work which properly belonged to the practical geologist or mining engineer, and for that reason could not undertake the examination of strictly private enterprises. I advised all prospectors, miners, and private companies engaged in promoting individual enterprises to secure the services of a competent scientific expert. But in case fifty taxpayers were sufficiently interested to ask for an examination of a certain region, I held myself in readiness to comply with the request.

During the three years I was with the survey, more than fifty different localities were examined and reports prepared on them. As a usual thing, one or two days were spent by some member of the staff in the examination of a particular region,

155

after which a public address was given, setting forth the conditions as they were found to exist. A report was written and usually published in the local newspaper. As a result of these examinations, several oil fields were opened up, sites for cement plants, lime kilns, and brick plants were located, cities were advised as to water supply, coal beds were traced, and an attempt was made to aid in developing the mineral resources of the state. Frequently we were able to find nothing of value, and we advised those interested not to spend money in useless prospecting.

It was about this time that farmers began plowing up the buffalo-grass sod in the Panhandle counties and sowing the land to wheat. Reasoning as a geologist, this seemed to me to be a very unwise thing to do, and I fear I helped to make myself unpopular in calling the matter to the attention of the people of Oklahoma.

There should still be in the files of the president of the State Board of Agriculture a two-page letter written some time in 1908 or 1909 wherein I stated that in my judgment far too much acreage on the High Plains was being put into cultivation. I set forth the fact that it had taken Nature thousands of years to produce the natural sod covering, buffalo grass, found on the High Plains, that the soil was a very loose type, and easily carried by the wind, that high winds were common in that region, and that, if the soil were broken out, it would eventually give rise to dust storms.

The reply to my letter was short and to the point. It left no doubt as to the intent of the writer. In effect it said, "You may or may not be a good geologist; we do not know. But it is very evident that you know nothing about agriculture. Please mind your own business."

Paraphrasing Chaucer, "There was no more to say." But all this was before the Dust Bowl.

Very little work had been done on the clays of Oklahoma at the time of the organization of the survey. We knew that the state possessed a large amount and a great variety of clays, but no one knew where they were located or just what they were good for. Arrangements were made with the U. S. Bureau of Mines to aid in testing Oklahoma clays. L. C. Snider, the chemist of the survey, spent several weeks at the government laboratories at Pittsburgh, Pennsylvania, testing out clay samples which had been sent there from different parts of Oklahoma. More than one hundred samples of clay from practically all parts of the state were analyzed and the results published in Bulletin Number 7, written by Snider. This report showed that Oklahoma had plenty of clay for making brick and tile, and for the manufacture of Portland cement and pottery.

It was always my object to keep in touch with the school teachers of the state and to secure their co-operation. Many of the high schools were just being organized, and few of them had any collections whatever to illustrate the various mineral products of the state. The survey prepared duplicate sets of minerals, fossils, and rocks, containing about seventy-five specimens, showing the different materials of this kind found in Oklahoma. During the three years I was director of the survey, more than fifty of these sets were sent out to the various schools.

Another popular movement was the preparation of the mineral exhibit at the state fair at Oklahoma City. I made arrangements whereby the Geological Survey was to collect and install a mineral display. The state fair paid the freight and provided the exhibit space. The survey collected the minerals, arranged them, and kept men in the booth during the fair to explain the exhibits.

For two years, this mineral exhibit was located in a corner on the top floor of the main exposition building, but it grew to such size that it was given a separate building. The collection was popular and thousands came to the building and saw something of what Oklahoma possessed in the way of minerals.

The exhibit was abandoned in 1921 on change of administration by the authorities at the state fair, and many of the valuable specimens were hauled away and dumped into the river. This was without the knowledge of anyone connected with the Geological Survey.

During these years I had never lost interest in the Arbuckle Mountains. These are a three-act drama in stone. Here, as at few places in the world, we may study the great earth forces that "without haste and without rest" have been at work throughout geological time shaping our continent.

Suppose we visit the mountains. From Oklahoma City we take U. S. Highway 77 and drive south eighty miles, passing through Norman, Purcell, and Pauls Valley. South of Davis we cross the Washita River and enter the mountains. On our right we see rock ledges dipping north, standing on edge. We cross Honey Creek and climb a steep and winding grade to come out on top of the hill and look down on Turner Falls. Before us to the right is a high knob covered with trees, East Timbered Hills. This is the igneous core of the mountains. We spin on south along the highway across the top of the mountains, with massive beds of rock at our right and left. Finally we come to a sign by the roadside on which is shown the cross section of the Arbuckles. Still farther south we find other roadside signs, but now the rocks dip south. If we stop to read the signs we find that they describe the formations. Finally we round a curve, leaving the last rock ledge behind and start across the flat plain. We have crossed the Arbuckles.

So easy to do, but what do these rocks tell us? If we can interpret what we have seen, if we are able to translate the record of the rocks, we realize that we have experienced a drama of three acts, in stone. Let us epitomize these three acts.

Act I. Deposition:

Millions of years ago, "waters covered the face of the great deep." Sediments derived from lost continents whose very locations are unknown were washed into this sea. These sediments, pebbles, sand, mud, ooze, silt, and other debris carried by streams were spread out on the ocean bottom and piled up, layer upon layer, stratum upon stratum, bed upon bed, until more than twelve thousand feet of rocks had accumulated. One group of rocks known as the Arbuckle limestone is eight thousand feet thick, one of the thickest formations in the world. The Simpson series is made up largely of shale and sandstone, one bed of which, known as the Wilcox sand, is the great oil producer. Other formations, higher in the scale, are called Viola, Sylvan, Hunton, and Woodford, names familiar in the oil fields.

Act II. Elevation:

After the deposition of this great mass of sediments, there came a series of earth stresses, great thrusts, probably from the south. The level-lying strata, unable to withstand this tremendous force, buckled and broke. The entire mass was arched up like a giant blister, sixty miles long, on the earth's surface. A two-mile thickness of rocks was raised into a vast dome.

Act III. Erosion:

After the land had been raised above the water, Nature's tools, rain and wind, heat and cold, frost and running water, began to cut and carve away the rocks. First, the upper and outside layers were worn away, then those beneath, until all the beds had been cut through, exposing the underlying granite. Age after age, eon after eon, this earth-shaping process has gone on. Slowly but unremittingly Nature's saw and plane have been rasping away, exposing along the sides of the mountains the ribs of Oklahoma.

159

If one is outdoors on a dark night, what is the best way to look into a room? Why, through a window, of course! And the Arbuckle Mountains are a window in Oklahoma, where we may look downward two miles toward the center of the earth.

From the Washita River south of Davis to the summit of the mountain near the big sign showing the cross section, we go downward geologically over the upturned, cut-off edges of the rocks more than twelve thousand feet, and continuing south we climb back again, the two miles to the edge of the mountains.

Is it complicated? Yes. No. The story is written in stone. He who runs may read. If we use the seeing eye and the understanding mind it is not complicated, but easy.

I continued to make trips into the Arbuckles at every opportunity. During two summers, when Lois and Don were small, we spent several weeks camping in the mountains, either on Honey Creek below Turner Falls, or at Price's Falls.

Near the latter place there lived an old gentleman whom everybody called Uncle Johnny Wadkins. He always asked me to come and see him and "stay all night," and on one of my trips, as I sat by the wood fire in his little log cabin, he told me a story I have never forgotten. Uncle Johnny is a "squaw man," that is, a white man who married an Indian wife. He first came to Indian Territory soon after the Civil War. There was some mystery connected with his early life, but what it was no one ever learned. He made a good farm hand, was skillful with the ax, and so had no difficulty in finding work in the wild country of the Chickasaw Nation along Washita River.

After drifting about for a few years, he married an Indian girl, which was not unusual at that time. They built a log cabin near a mountain spring, cleared out a field or two, and for many years lived happily, as they understood happiness. Then the native instinct began to assert itself and the Indian wife became dissatisfied and morose and finally left her husband and children to go back to her own people. At the time of my story, Uncle Johnny lived with the younger children, two little girls and a boy of sixteen, in the old cabin. The older children had married and now lived on farms of their own. Occasionally the wife came back for a few days, but she was not contented and soon went back to her own people. Sometimes the little girls went back with her and stayed with their mother for a week or two, but they preferred the home they had always known, and so lived with their father for the greater part of the year.

Uncle Johnny was a tall, spare man about seventy years of age, with hair and grizzled beard white as snow, and kindly light blue eyes which twinkled under shaggy brows. As he told me the story, he sat bent over in his low, split-bottomed chair with a hickory "pokin' stick" in his hand. As the fire burned low, he stirred up the hickory logs, which snapped and crackled and sent up tongues of yellow flame, throwing into strong relief the meagerly furnished room. In the center of the cabin stood a rough table, by the wall was a cupboard containing a few dishes. Two four-poster beds stood in corners. In one of them the two little girls were already asleep. The boy, Billie, sat nodding by the fire. Long before the story was finished, he had climbed the ladder behind the door to his bed in the loft. The other bed was for Uncle Johnny and me. A hound dog lay on the floor with his nose pointed toward the fire, and a black and white kitten was purring between Uncle Johnny's feet. And this is the story. I have tried to put it into his own language:

"I reckin ye seen that ole cabin just acrost the river from here, on Possom Flats. I mean the one standin' out in the field by itself with the chimbly all fell down. Did you ever hear tell the story about that thar cabin? No, reckin not. That's the place where Pete Nolan stood off the marshals. They haint been nobody livin' there for nigh about twenty year, an' so far ez I can rec'lect, they's only me an' old Jim Hunter, that's a livin' with his youngest boy Sam up on Wild Hoss above the old fort, that was here when that cabin was built. It's been, let me see, it's been forty-one year come corn-plantin' time since that thar cabin was put up.

"Pete Nolan built that cabin. They uster call 'im Texas Pete an' Big Pete, 'cause the word got out that he come from Texas, an' he was a strappin' big feller; must a weighed nigh about two hundred er two hundred an' twenty-five pound, an' a fine-built man as ye most ever seen, stout ez a bar an' wan't afeard o' nothin' ner nobody. Folks uster wonder whatever possessed Pete to build away out on the level, away from anybody er any trees, but he was one of them kind a' fellers that 'tended to his own business, an' in them days nobody took it onto theirselves to meddle with other folkses affairs, an' so after a spell the thing was dropped, an' folks 'peared to fergit all about it.

"Ez near ez I kin rec'lect he must o' lived thar three year, er mebby four, and a might good neighbor he was, allers willin' to sheer such ez he had with them ez had less. Thar wasn't many settlers here them days, an' it 'peared ez if folks wuz more sociable like than they are now. I was a young feller then, sasshayin' roun', sorter shiftless, I reckin, sometimes here an' sometimes there, at home wherever my hat was off, an' I used to sorter drop in on Pete right often. Alwas glad to see a feller, an' liked to listen to him talk, too, but he never did say much hisself. One a' these sorta quiet fellers that 'pear to enjoy lettin' the other feller do all the talkin', and sometimes they're the sociablest kind they is.

"His wife was a mighty fine lookin' woman, must 'a not been mor'n twenty or twenty-one when they fust come to the country, an' purty ez a picture. I don't remember ever seein' a purtier woman nowhere, black eyes, an' long black hair, a fine-built woman, an' she allas 'peared to think a heap of Pete and him o' her. I reck'n she wuz the best cook anywhere in the

162

Gould and the first Geological Library at the University of
Oklahoma, destroyed by fire, 1903.

Geology students above Turner Falls in the Arbuckles, 1909.

Geology students in camp near White Mound, 1909.

country in them days. What venison that woman could fry! and Johnny cake, too! Wild turkeys was ez plenty ez chickens is now, an' she certainly did know how to bake turkey afore the fire. I kin rec'lect just ez well how she uster look when she was a cookin' on the hearth with the fire makin' her face all red, an' how the vittles tasted when she sot 'em on the table.

"A young feller knockin' 'round from piller to post like I wuz in them days, an' doin' his own cookin', what little he gets done, gets mighty keen fer a good meal's vittles once in a while. I've sometimes thought that it must 'a' been seein' Pete's wife so much an' a eatin' her cookin' that made me think about marryin' when I did, only I didn't get no such woman as Pete's. They didn't never have no children and as matters turned out it was well enough the' didn't.

"Well, ez I was sayin' Pete and his wife must 'a' lived in that cabin over thar three, or mebby four, year, and none of us never did knew fer sure whar they come from no more nothin' in the world, though the word got out they come from Texas, fer Pete ner the woman never let out no hint, and ez I said we didn't enquire much in them days what a man's business was, ner whar he come from. Pete never did much farmin' to speak of, mebby he'd raise a garden, or a little tom fuller patch, but not nigh enough to do him. Never seemed to want fer money, but in them days a little money went a mighty long ways, an' a man that was handy with a rifle could get his livin' outer the woods. He always conducted hisself straight when he was here, so far ez I ever heard, an' none of us never suspected nothin'.

"They was always marshals a comin' and a goin', ridin' through the country lookin' fer hoss thieves an' outlaws an' sich, an' onct in a while some of 'em would put up overnight with Pete. In them days they was the gov'ment marshals from Fort Smith, and the Texas marshals, rangers they called 'em, from sommers down in Texas. I never did rightly know whar their

163

headquarters was, Paris, mebby. They was a band of hoss thieves that used up on the head of Wild Hoss an' the marshals had two or three shootin' scrapes up that way, not far from the old fort, an' some was hurt on both sides, and mebby some was killed, I most fergit now, but anyway they never did break up the gang, not till long after.

"In them days the marshals sorter divided the country between them, an' the gov'ment marshal kept north of the mountains, an' worked the country between here an' the Canadian, an' the Texas marshals stayed south of the mountains an' looked after everything ez fer ez Red River. They had a sort o' headquarters at old man Simpkins place down near the mouth o' Caddo, the Texas marshals did, an' we didn't very often see any o' 'em up in these parts, although onct in a while one would ride through lookin' fer a hoss thief or somethin' like that.

"Nobody never did know jist how it happened, fer o' course the marshals never did tell how they found out whar Pete wuz a livin' at, an' so the fust thing we knowed, one day they wuz about twenty o' 'em had his place surrounded an' he was a standin' 'em off. I rec'lect it was in summer just as corn was a tasslin' out. They'd all rid up in the airly part o' the night an' tied their hosses in a bunch of persimmon bushes down by the river and crawled up behind stumps and things, an' some of 'em behind his barn, and they planned to wait till daylight an' then get Pete when he come out.

"But Pete's dogs smelt 'em and begun barkin' along about the middle of the night, an' Pete got up and peeked out through a chink; the moon was a shinin' an' he seen what was a goin' on, an' got his wife up an' they dressed, an' before the marshals knowed they was awake they commenced shootin' at 'em. Pete always kept three er four guns in the house an' never went nowhere without a gun an' a pistol, but we never thought nothin' o' that, fer we all did the same thing in them days. He knocked the chinkin' out between the logs so's he could shoot, an' he stood on the side of the house where most o' the marshals was, an' his wife she stood on the other side, an' they kept a shootin' so fast, an' both o' 'em was good shots, that the marshals didn't dast show themselves, an' Pete an' his wife kept them thar on the ground behind the stumps all that day. The marshals kep' a shootin' too, an' I s'pose they must a' pumped nigh onto a half bushel o' lead into that ole cabin, but they never did hit Pete ner his wife onct. They got some o' the marshals though; killed one, I believe, and wounded three er four more in the laigs, where they was stickin' out behind the stumps.

"Ez soon ez it got dark an' Pete couldn't see to shoot straight no more the marshals pulled out an' left. They got on their hosses, an' rid all night carrying their wounded on hossback, an' it was mornin' when they got back to ole man Simpkinses, an' I heard that two o' the marshals Pete had wounded was so shot up that they died, the next day.

"When Pete heard 'em leavin', him an' his wife never waited fer nothin' but they pulled out the same night, an' made fer the mountains, and tuck up with ole Bully July, a old renegade outlaw nigger that had a camp on the head of Colbert Creek, close to West Timbered Hills. He'd killed dozens o' men, so folks said, an' the marshals was all anxious to take 'im, but they was all afeard of 'im, leastwise they never tackled 'im no more. He was always a harborin' a lot o' outlaw niggers an' whites, an' hoss thieves and sich, an' they all looked up to Bully July an' whatever he said went.

"Pete an' his wife they come to Bully's camp an' Bully took 'em in an' harbored 'em an' fed 'em fer a week er two. Pete was anxious to get away, fer his wife was the only woman in the camp an' he didn't feel safe to leave 'er alone. One day, Bully and Pete went out huntin' turkeys an' Pete, he never did come back. Bully said he fell over a cliff an' killed hisself, but young

Jim Jackson, ole man Jackson's boy that lived up on Buckhorn, who'd been stealin' hosses and was hidin' from the marshals in Bully's camp, was out huntin' that very same day, an' he claimed that he seen Bully July shoot Pete in the back an' throw him over the rocks. Bully got to hear what young Jim'd said an' so he took the boy out an' killed him the next day. After that Bully kept Pete's wife in his camp fer mighty nigh a month, till the woman seen there waren't no chance to git away, an' so one night she up an' cut her own throat with a butcher knife.

"When ole man Jackson heard that Bully'd killed his boy he done pulled out fer Fort Smith an' fixed up a scheme with the marshals there to get Bully. They waited a month er two so that Bully'd not be suspicious, an' then they sent out ole Buck Peters an' a possy o' marshals, an' ole Buck's rule was that when he went after a man, he got the man or else the man got him. So the marshals come with ole man Jackson, and him and Buck Peters they went down south of the mountains to whar some niggers lived that knowed where Bully's camp was, to git 'em to carry word to Bully July. The niggers was skeered to death of Bully fer he'd threatened time an' agin to kill 'em if they ever so much ez let on like they knowed whar he stayed, but Buck he hired one of the young niggers to carry word up to Bully that Buck wanted him to help ketch the gang of hoss thieves up on the head o' Wild Hoss.

"Bully sent back word that if Buck wanted anything of him he'd have to come up to the camp an' talk it over. Ole man Jackson an' all the rest of 'em tried their best to keep Buck from goin', fur Bully'd killed two or three men in just that way, gettin' 'em to come up an' talk with 'im and they never did come back; but Buck he went an' the rest of 'em 'lowed they'd never see 'im alive again. Nobody never did find out from Buck how he did it, but he got Bully persuaded to go an' help take them hoss thieves. Some says he offered to give Bully a thousand dollars if

166

he'd go along, an' some says he promised to git 'im pardoned, fer Bully was gettin' mighty tired o' scoutin' an' hidin' out, but anyhow Buck got 'em to promise to meet 'im up here at the mouth o' Honey Creek an' go with 'im an' the marshals an' git the hoss thieves.

"Well Bully come to whar he said he would, an' them that seen him says he was the biggest nigger they ever seen, weighed more'n three hundred pounds, an' a ridin' a big red stallion with two white feet that some o' his men had stole sommers down in Texas.

"Bully was allers mighty suspicious, an' he made all the marshals ride ahead an' he follered along behind 'em with a gun over his arm like they was his prisoners. Buck had it all fixed up that they was to take Bully when he done went to sleep that fust night, an' he tole his men fer all o' 'em to lay down like they was goin' to sleep, but to stay awake till Bully was asleep. Bully made him a bed off by hisself away from the marshals an' laid down with his gun by his side an' two pistols cocked by his piller, an' a knife in his belt. Buck an' his men all laid down an' pretended like they was asleep an' listened till they heard Bully begin to snore, an' then they all crawled up quiet, so's not to wake him, an' they grabbed his we'pons away an' all piled on top o' him. They say it tuck the whole bunch of 'em to tie 'im fer he was a powerful man an' fit terrible, but finally they overpowered 'im and hogtied 'im.

"They didn't wait till morning, fer they was afeard that some o' Bully's men would try to take him back, but they got a wagon an' team from one o' the settlers, an' hauled him hogtied in the bottom o' the wagon all the way to Fort Smith, more'n three hundred miles. They never stopped on the way fer the hoss thieves ner nothin' but rode day an' night, an' ez soon ez one of the hosses give out, they picked up another from the settlers an' marshals they met till they got Bully July safe in jail at Fort

Smith. Next term o' court he was tried before Judge Parker, the one they called the hangin' judge, an' they hung him on the old gallows in the stockade, whar they say that more'n a hundred outlaws an' murderers had been hung.

"I never did rightly learn what the Texas marshals was after Pete Nolan fer. Some says he was jist a common hoss thief down about San Antone, an' some says he had killed a man down in the San Saba country an' run off with his wife, an' that the woman he had here wasn't his wife at all. Nobody ever knowed the straight o' it as fer as I ever did hear. But if you'll chop into one of them logs in that ole cabin over on Possom Flats, you'll find some of the bullets that was shot at Pete an' the woman the day when they stood the marshals off."

But to return to things geological:—The first few years after the organization of the Oklahoma Geological Survey, I had considerable difficulty in securing co-operation from the federal authorities at Washington. Oklahoma appeared to be in bad repute with governmental officials. Each year large amounts of money are appropriated by Congress for geological work throughout the United States, and many of the state surveys co-operate with the U. S. Geological Survey in the investigation and publication of data regarding mineral resources. Having failed to get results by correspondence, I made a special trip to Washington to interview the authorities of the U. S. Geological Survey, but it was only after a number of interviews that I secured a small appropriation. Senator Robert L. Owen was instrumental in helping to secure this aid. The next year it was not so difficult to get co-operation.

Arrangements were made with the U. S. Geological Survey for an investigation of the oil fields of northern Oklahoma, and it was planned to prepare maps and write reports on the Nowata Quadrangle. For the third summer Professor Ohern had charge of the work in this region. His assistants were Everett Carpenter, R. H. Wood, J. C. Thompson, C. W. Hamilton, and John Herald. Chester A. Reeds continued his work in the Arbuckle Mountains.

The work of the Oklahoma Survey went on as usual during the winter of 1910–11. Hutchison had been at work for some months on the preparation of a report on the oil and asphalt deposits of the state. His connection with the Survey terminated in November before the publication of his report, which appeared as Bulletin Number 2, and L. C. Snider was advanced to the position of assistant state geologist. Frank Buttram, a graduate student, took his place as chemist.

It was on one of my trips into western Oklahoma that I first saw Coyote Butte, two miles east of Geary, which stands sentinel over the beautiful valley of the North Canadian River. This butte is held up by a ledge of white dolomite, which, being harder than the soft sandstone of the country, has withstood the action of the force of erosion. It is the last vanishing remnant of a plain that once occupied all this region.

In the late seventies, when the Cheyenne and Arapahoe Indians were finally persuaded to cease roaming the plains and settle down on reservations, the land assigned to them included part of the valley of the North Canadian. Darlington was the seat of the Cheyenne Agency, and many of the Indians had their tipis in the timber along the river bottoms.

The Cheyennes were very much excited during the Messiah craze in 1890. They held meetings, sometimes secret, but often in the open, and the medicine men, who could not forget the old days when the buffalo roamed the plains, played on the feelings of their tribesmen to persuade them to prepare for the coming of the Messiah, and to arm themselves and throw off the white man's yoke.

Many of the meetings were held on or near Coyote Butte,

169

a famous landmark and gathering place for the tribe. Great preparations were made for receiving the Messiah when he should come.

The most impressive thing was the fact that the Indians prepared a bed for their coming Lord. They got an iron bedstead with springs, mattress, and blankets, protected by a tent, and set them up on top of Coyote Butte, where they remained for several years until demolished by the wind and rain.

When someone asked why they prepared this bed, one of the old men of the tribe explained.

"When white man's God came to this world to visit his children he was poor man. He had no house. He had no bed. He had no money. Little bird had nest in tree. Coyote had hole under rock. But white man's God had no place to sleep.

"We are better than white man. When our God comes, maybe so tomorrow, maybe so next moon, he find that we his people have bed for him."

Provision for the maintenance of the Oklahoma Geological Survey for the following two years was made in the general appropriation bill, in which $18,800 a year was appropriated for the work. Governor Cruce approved the bill and four parties were placed in the field.

Professor Ohern continued in the northern part of the state, working on the geology of the Vinita Quadrangle. As assistants he had John Herald, J. B. Newby, Glenn C. Clark, and Robert E. Garrett. This work was done in co-operation with the U. S. Geological Survey.

An examination of the building stone and mineral resources of the Wichita Mountains was undertaken by Professor Taylor. This work also was carried on under agreement with the United States Geological Survey. His assistants were Frank Buttram, M. L. McCance, and B. H. West. Chester A. Reeds again spent the summer in the Arbuckle Mountains. He had already published, as Bulletin Number 3 of the Survey, a report entitled the *Mineral Resources of the Arbuckle Mountains,* but wished to spend more time studying the paleontology of the region. Burr McWhirt was his assistant.

My friend Beede spent the greater part of the summer studying the red beds of the state. These formations underlie practically all the western half of Oklahoma, and at that time comparatively little was known as to their nature. J. C. Thompson and George H. Myer were Beede's assistants.

It was during the fall of 1911 that I finally decided to discontinue work for the state and to engage in the private practice of my profession. There were several reasons for making this change. One reason was that my health was beginning to suffer. For twenty years I had been under constant strain, first as a student attempting to work my way through school, then as a teacher in the University, building up a department, and finally for three years as state geologist, fighting the battles of the survey. During this time I had had practically no vacation, but had worked almost day and night. A holiday for me had come to mean a time when students and other people were out of the way and I was free to work for myself. My general health had been good, and I had been able, in the main, to meet all the demands made upon me, but I had begun to realize that there is a limit to one's power of endurance.

A second reason for making the change was that I was tired of fighting politicans. I have never possessed any of the instincts of a politician, always preferring to work by direction rather than by indirection. I had a constant and strenuous fight to keep the survey out of politics, and to keep it free to do the work for which it had been organized. My acquaintance over the state was quite extensive and I had been able to receive from the Legislature sufficient funds to carry on the survey work in a limited way. I had begun to feel that the results obtained were not worth the effort.

In the days of my inexperience, I had thought that, when I once had a bunch of politicians whipped into line, the work was completed. It took me several years to learn that there is nothing new in politics, except the faces; that a new bunch, mostly honest but woefully ignorant, come up to the Legislature every two years; that they are herded like sheep by a few ringleaders who know exactly what they want and how to get it, and are put away in their proper pigeon holes and told when to come out and vote. I wished to be a free man once more and to be able to look a politician in the eye and tell him where to go, and to know that my position depended neither upon his influence nor upon his vote.

My third reason was financial. The year that I began teaching at the University I received $400 for the year's work. My salary had been raised to $1,200, to $1,320, to $1,500, and finally for two years before I became state geologist, to $1,800. The Geological Survey Commission fixed my salary at $2,500. Earlier in life this amount looked big to me, but as my salary increased, my expenses increased with it, and I always had difficulty in coming out even at the end of the year. In this regard my experience was not different from that of other men in public life. Perhaps not one in ten of the school teachers or public officials engaged in state or government work make anything but a bare living. I had received an offer to enter work in a private company at a salary practically twice that which I was receiving, and I did not feel justified in refusing it.

The fourth reason was that, to some extent, I had achieved my ambitions. While I was in college I set for myself three tasks: To occupy a chair of geology in a state university, to be state geologist of some state, and to know the geology and mineral resources of the southern part of the Great Plains. Two of

172

these things I had accomplished within ten years after graduating from college; and I believed that the other one could better be done as a free lance, not tied down to a single state. I had given more than ten of the best years of my life to Oklahoma, and I saw no reason why I should not resign from state work and devote myself to the practice of my profession. There seemed to be nothing more to be gained in public life, and I was becoming tired of the game, and beginning to go stale.

My wife and I had discussed the matter pro and con for months. She realized better than I that the work was beginning to tell on my strength, and she was quite anxious that I shift the responsibility. I did not know, until several years later, that our physician had warned her that unless she wished to collect on my life insurance, she had better get me away from survey work. I could not then understand why she suddenly became so insistent that I resign.

My great concern was that I might not be able to make a living for the family. I had been in public service for so many years, coming up at the end of the month and getting my pay check, that I was really afraid to trust myself. Many a man in public life has had this fear, and I venture to say that were it not for the bread and butter question, many of those now engaged in teaching and other forms of public service, would seize the first opportunity to quit and go into private life.

I was extremely anxious that the Oklahoma Geological Survey should fall into good hands, for I naturally did not wish to see the institution that I had built up by years of effort collapse for want of proper direction. I discussed the matter with Governor Lee Cruce, telling him of my intention of resigning. He was quite anxious that I reconsider my decision and remain with the survey, but when I explained the situation he acquiesced in my plans. Lee Cruce was one of the cleanest and most conscientious men ever in public life in Oklahoma.

173

The man whom I wished to succeed me as director of the survey was Professor Ohern. To my mind he was the one man in Oklahoma at that time pre-eminently qualified to carry on the work. He had shown himself to be a good executive. He had become well acquainted with the geology of the state. He was a genial, companionable man, a convincing speaker, a splendid mixer, much better than I have ever been, and was in all ways eminently fitted to become state geologist.

I presented to the commission my resignation as director of the Geological Survey of Oklahoma on October 6, 1911, and on my recommendation Professor Ohern was appointed to the position. I shall always be proud of the unsolicited testimonial which the commission gave me on accepting my resignation. It was prepared by Dean Julien C. Monnet and signed by all members of the commission:

Memorial Concerning Ex-State Geologist
CHARLES N. GOULD

Dr. Charles N. Gould, Director of the Geological Survey of the State of Oklahoma, having just resigned that position, the undersigned members of the Oklahoma Geological Survey Commission take pleasure in filing this testimonial of our appreciation of the character of Dr. Gould and of the work he has done for the State. Dr. Gould received his bachelor's degree from Southwestern Kansas College in 1889 and his A.M. from the University of Nebraska in 1900, and his Ph.D. from the latter school in 1906. He is a Fellow of the Geological Society of America and of the American Association for the Advancement of Science. He was Vice President of the American Mining Congress from 1908 to 1911. He came to the University of Oklahoma in 1900 and occupied the chair of geology. He was engaged in field work for the Territorial Geological Survey in the summers of 1900, 1902, and 1906, and conducted field parties for the United States Geological Survey in the summers of 1901, 1903, 1904, and 1905. As professor and head of the Department of Geology in the University he built up that department very greatly from 1900 to 1908, during the time he was in charge, and turned out a number of excellent young men, many of whom are now distinguishing themselves in other schools and in the service of the government as geologists.

Twenty years ago Dr. Gould set for himself the task of knowing as well as any man might know, the geology and mineral resources of the southern part of the Great Plains west of the Mississippi River, and he has accomplished that task in a remarkable manner and is today regarded as possessing the greatest fund of information concerning the geological section of the country in which Oklahoma is located and especially of Oklahoma itself, of any man past or present.

He was instrumental in securing a constitutional provision for a Geological Survey. He wrote the law under which the present Survey operates, and he has done everything in his power to keep the Survey on the basis of scholarly science, nor has it at any time been subject to any deteriorating influences. He was appointed Director of the Survey July 25th, 1908, and his resignation was accepted with great regret by the undersigned October 7, 1911. During his incumbency he published widely on the subject of geology and the mineral resources of Oklahoma. His writings include nearly two hundred titles counting government reports, state reports, and numerous scientific and popular articles, covering a wide range of subjects. During all that time he has always had a reputation for conservatism. He has never rushed into print with ill-founded conclusions, but has first secured all his facts and then carefully studied their relationships before announcing the result. Dr. Gould is a scholar of broad scientific attainments. The State of

Oklahoma has experienced the loss of a most valuable servant in his resignation.

THE OKLAHOMA GEOLOGICAL SURVEY
COMMISSION
(Signed) Lee Cruce, Governor
(Signed) R. H. Wilson, State Superintendent
of Public Instruction
(Signed) Julien C. Monnet, Acting President
University of Oklahoma

Professor Ohern remained director of the Oklahoma Geological Survey for about two years. Snider was assistant director, C. W. Shannon, who had come to Norman to accept a position with the survey a few months before I resigned, was field geologist, and Frank Buttram, chemist. At the end of two years, Professor Ohern received an offer to go into the oil business and resigned January 1, 1914, taking Buttram with him. The position of director was offered to Snider, who declined it in order to attend graduate school and secure his doctor's degree. It was then offered to Shannon, who accepted and continued in the position until 1923, when the appropriations for the survey were vetoed by Governor Walton a few months before he was impeached.

I have always considered L. C. Snider, who was the first chemist of the survey and for a number of years assistant director, to be one of the best scientists who ever came to Oklahoma. He wrote a number of reports of high order. Bulletin Number 7, *Clay and Clay Industries of Oklahoma;* Bulletin Number 8, *Road Material and Road Conditions of Oklahoma;* Bulletin Number 9, *Lead and Zinc in Oklahoma;* Bulletin Number 11, *Gypsum in Oklahoma,* and Bulletin Number 17, *Geography of Oklahoma,* are all from his versatile pen. For several

176

years he was engaged in the study of some very technical problems, connected with the paleontology and stratigraphy of certain formations of northeastern Oklahoma, and later secured his doctorate from the University of Chicago. He afterward resigned from the survey, and became chief geologist and technical adviser to one of the leading public utilities men in America. He is now a member of the Department of Geology at the University of Texas.

At the time of my resignation from the survey and Professor Ohern's promotion to the directorship, Professor Charles H. Taylor was made head of the Department of Geology.

And so, after eleven strenuous and happy years on the campus, I quit state service, leaving both the department and the survey in capable hands.

CHAPTER 8

THIRTEEN YEARS IN
CONSULTING PRACTICE

ABOUT THE TIME I RESIGNED from the survey, the science of petroleum geology began to be recognized in this country. In the early days of the oil industry, wells were located by guess, or by hunches. Some men followed "creekology," using the forked stick or the magic wand.

The term "doodlebug" was used to describe any sort of mechanical device which was supposed to locate oil or any other mineral substance under ground. One old oilman once told me that his favorite method of locating a well was to tie a tin can to a dog's tail and start the dog on a run across the prairie. Where the can came off, there he would drill.

During the two decades at the turn of the century, geologists began to realize that there was often a definite relation between surface conditions of the rocks and deposits of petroleum underground. I. C. White, the state geologist of West Virginia, and other geologists, promulgated the theory that oil occurred under anticlines. At first this theory was ridiculed not only by practical oilmen but by many geologists as well. But, as time passed and more and more oil fields were brought in, the relations of the deposits of petroleum to the structure of the rocks were studied, and it became evident that the anticlinal theory had merit, and after a few years it became generally accepted.

178

D. W. Ohern, right, and his Geological Survey party, 1910.

Gould searching for fossils, 1926.

At the time I entered professional work, there were but three men in Oklahoma who were doing work along this line. Several years earlier, J. H. Goodrich had located the Wheeler Oil Field near Ardmore, and Pierce Larkin and L. L. Hutchison, both former students of mine, were beginning geological work at Tulsa.

I became a member of a company formed for the purpose of locating and developing oil and other mineral resources in the Southwest. For some months, Nina, the children, and I lived at Muskogee. Oil leases were taken on an anticline near Warner, in southeastern Muskogee County; a well was drilled which encountered both oil and gas, but not in commercial quantities. Other prospective properties were located, but we were not successful in securing profitable production. The company was under-financed, the executives inexperienced in the oil business, and after a year the company ceased operation.

I then became associated with some Oklahoma City businessmen, who organized the Mid-Continent Company. We spent about two years in exploratory work, chiefly in Oklahoma, but no profitable oil production was secured. While in the employ of this company, I made a trip to Mexico for the purpose of inspecting a tract of land north of Tampico. This *hacienda,* or ranch, of approximately 750,000 acres, was as large as an Oklahoma county. On this entire *hacienda* I saw only two four-wheeled vehicles, one was a sort of broad-wheeled truck for hauling sugar cane, the other a stagecoach drawn by six mules, two on the wheel and four in the lead. From the main head-quarters of the ranch, one rode in the stagecoach as far as there were any roads, then took a saddle horse and rode twenty miles farther, to the edge of the property.

If I were asked to describe my idea of torture, I would say riding one of those abominable Mexican saddles the first few days. On these trips, Carlos, my *mozo,* was my *alter ego.* Always on hand, smiling, cheerful, willing, anticipating my every want, he was my man. In Mexico, you are assigned a *mozo*, a personal attendant, a servant. He helps prepare your food, he stands behind your table and serves you when you eat, he looks after your horse, and, when traveling, he rides at a respectful distance behind you.

We rode day after day through the tall grass and luxuriant vegetation. Never have I seen such fertile soil. It was practically undeveloped. On this tract of land there were only half a dozen farms in cultivation. Two crops of corn were grown each year, tomato plants live to be four years old, and all sorts of citrus fruits flourished. The wild *limón*, or lime, was common, and day after day, winding our way through the bottom lands, our horses' hoofs crushed tens of thousands of limes which had ripened and fallen to the ground. Oh, the limeades that never were made!

Some two thousand *peóns* lived on this *hacienda*, but probably not more than a dozen of this number could read or write. Natives they were, of pure Indian stock, with practically no admixture of Spanish or other white blood, and only a very thin veneer of Spanish civilization; quiet, inoffensive, home-loving, peaceful people, wanting nothing but to be let alone, very different from our ideas derived from the movies and Wild West stories of the blood-thirsty Mexican with a knife, a rifle, and a belt full of cartridges. The tides of commerce had passed them by, but they were happy and contented, totally without ambition or the desire to "better their condition."

Carlos was of this breed. More intelligent than most, he was a fine character and I learned to respect and admire him. He knew no English and I spoke no Spanish. According to custom, I had taken with me a Spanish phrase book and dictionary, but it did not take long to learn that conversation *a la* phrase book is a snare and delusion. I hit upon the following plan. As we rode along, I would point to some near-by object, and Carlos would give me the Spanish name. A cow was *"la vaca, señor,"* a tree was *"mesquite, señor,"* or *"cedro,"* or *"ebano."* He was always polite, always pleasant, trying to please me. I would hold up one finger, *"uno, señor,"* two fingers, *"dos, señor,"* three fingers, *"tres, señor,"* and so on. By the end of the first week, Carlos and I were holding extended conversations.

I had trouble persuading Carlos to ride beside me, for, according to tradition, his place was in the rear. When I would suggest his coming up alongside, he would say respectfully but firmly, "No, señor, no." I finally got tired trying to talk over my shoulder and spoke sharply. With reluctance he rode up beside me, and as long as I was trying to carry on a conversation, he would remain there, but as soon as I ceased talking, he would quietly fall behind.

The *tortilla,* a flat corn-cake something like a southern john-niecake, is the native food of Mexico. The *peóns* eat *tortillas* three times a day, and one of the chief articles of furniture in the poorer class Mexican home is the *metate,* or flat grinding stone, for making *tortilla* meal. Going past at meal time one sees and hears the woman grinding away at the cracked corn. When a handful of corn has been reduced to meal, she rolls and pats it flat in the form of a little round cake, which she bakes on a charcoal stove.

When one sits at meals, there is a little stack of *tortillas* before him, and while he eats, the woman keeps on baking and bringing others. *Tortillas* often serve as plates upon which are served the *carne* or stewed meats. I have seen a folded *tortilla* used as a spoon or ladle, to convey portions of stew into the mouth, and after a meal the fingers wiped on a *tortilla* which is then thrown to the dogs.

At a Mexican meal, in addition to *tortillas* and *carne* (always stewed), there is usually *caso,* which is unripened goat's milk cheese, and *cafe,* black sweetened coffee with the *dulce* or sugar cooked with it, which looks and tastes like a thick, sweet syrup. Milk is never used cold, but is always heated before serving.

I was at one of the little *rancheros,* or sub-ranches, twenty miles from the main *hacienda.* Carlos and I had been riding all afternoon and at nightfall we came to a cluster of brush houses, open on two sides, where lived a *caporal,* or under-foreman, and several *vaqueros,* or cowboys, with their families, and a few pigs, chickens and goats. The cattle had been rounded up for the night and driven into the corral. Carlos spoke to the *caporal* and he in turn gave instructions for the women to prepare a meal for us. Corn grinding began and soon the *tortillas* were ready.

A table was placed under a tree and I sat down while Carlos stood at my elbow. Just then it began to rain. Willing hands carried the table under the roof, where it was placed among the kids (human and goat), chickens, and pigs. I then started my meal. The usual black *cafe* was in evidence. Now I like cream in my coffee, but if there is no cream, milk will serve.

"Carlos," said I, "*leche.*"

"No, *señor,*" replied Carlos, "no *leche.*"

"*Si,* Carlos, *leche,*" said I.

"No *leche, señor,*" repeated Carlos, respectfully but firmly.

I pointed to the corral about fifty yards away where all the cattle were standing.

"*La vaca,* Carlos, *leche, la vaca.*"

Finally Carlos seemed to catch the drift of my remarks; he understood that I wanted him to milk the cow. He grabbed an earthen jar, paddled out through the drizzling rain, tackled the first cow he found, did business with her for a few minutes, came back with about a pint of fresh milk in the jar and handed it to the woman to heat on the fire.

"*Leche,* Carlos," I said.

"*Si, señor, leche caliente* (hot milk)."

"No," I told him. "*Leche frio* (cold milk)."

"No, *señor*, no. No *leche frio, leche caliente*," Carlos maintained.

And do you know, he wouldn't give me the fresh milk. I had to get up from the table and take it from the woman's hand. The natives stared in astonishment at the stranger who dared to drink unheated milk. But I had milk for my coffee.

When I had finished my investigation and was ready to leave I gave Carlos two *pesos*, equal to about one dollar in American money. He was as pleased as a little boy with a stick of candy, and bowed and said, "*Mucho gracias, señor, mucho, mucho.*" And when the train pulled out the last thing I saw was Carlos standing on the platform, hat in hand, bowing, "*Adiós, señor, adiós.*"

How nearly one may come to securing something worthwhile and yet miss it was illustrated by one incident that occurred while I was working with the Mid-Continent. I was driving in a two-horse buggy, scouting the country and hunting anticlines between Ardmore and Waurika in eastern Jefferson and western Carter counties. Headquarters were at a hotel in the little inland town of Cornish, which has since passed out of existence. I had been working in the jack-oak country some miles northeast of Cornish, and late one afternoon I found some beds of sandstone dipping southwest. I knew this indicated I was probably on the edge of an anticline, and that the axis of the structure lay somewhere to the northeast.

The hour was late and I was obliged to start back in order to reach my hotel before dark. On arriving I found a long-distance telephone call concerning a well that was being drilled in eastern Nowata County. I drove to Ardmore, arriving at one o'clock in the morning, and proceeded by train to Nowata, drove to the well and found that it had come in dry. My long trip was of no avail.

On my return to Oklahoma City, I explained to the men in the office that I believed I had found something northeast of Cornish which might possibly develop into an oil field, and suggested that I go back and spend a few days working it out. At that time, southern Oklahoma was not in good repute as an oil country, and after an office conference, it was decided not to spend any more money prospecting in that region. I protested and tried to explain, but nothing I could say would change the opinion of the "hard-headed businessmen."

Within six months, the first producing well in the Healdton Oil Field was drilled within a mile of the place where I had seen the rocks dipping southwest, and this field soon afterwards became one of the major oil fields of Oklahoma. I have never doubted that, had I been permitted to go back and follow up what I had discovered, the company would have owned a considerable part of the Healdton Oil Field.

The Mid-Continent Company was unsuccessful in securing production, and soon thereafter was discontinued. I opened an office as consulting geologist in the Colcord Building, Oklahoma City, where I practiced my profession until 1924. During this time my work extended over a considerable portion of the central part of the United States, including Oklahoma, Texas, Kansas, New Mexico, Montana, Arkansas, Missouri, Kentucky, Tennessee, Mississippi, and Louisiana. While this work consisted chiefly of the attempt to locate anticlines and other structures considered favorable for the production of oil, "all was fish that came to the geologist's net," and I accepted a number of commissions on things other than petroleum.

One of the first bits of research work I did after opening my office was for a company owned by the late Henry L. Doherty, who then controlled a number of utilities in the Middle West.

He had bought three gas companies, all of which were taking gas from the former Hogshooter Field near Bartlesville, serving Wichita and other cities in southern Kansas, the smelters at Iola, and with pipe lines extending to Miami, Joplin, and other towns in the lead-and-zinc district.

Mr. Doherty sent from Pittsburgh a young engineer, Alfred J. Discher, as manager. He established an office at Bartlesville but soon found that these companies had everything that well-regulated gas companies needed except gas. There were pipe lines, and pumping stations, and contracts, and payrolls to be met, but the wells in the Hogshooter Field were nearly exhausted, and were going into salt water about two per month.

Mr. Discher sent out a Macedonian cry for help, and as a result I entered into a contract with him on a retainer and *per diem* basis to search for gas. As assistant, I secured Everett Carpenter, who was then in the employ of the U. S. Geological Survey at Washington. He came to Oklahoma and the two of us started out attempting to locate anticlines which might produce gas.

We worked over Osage County and several counties in southern Kansas, locating among others, anticlines at Dexter, Cambridge, and Beaumont. We also examined two small gas wells a few miles southeast of Augusta, Kansas, which had been located purely by chance, and drilled by local capital, the gas being used to supply the town of Augusta. When the Wichita Gas Company was organized, the Augusta franchise, including the two wells, was absorbed into the larger company.

Carpenter and I hired a team and buggy, and for several days drove over the country. To our surprise, we discovered that these gas wells chanced to be located on the northeast end of a well-marked anticline, which we were able to follow southwest over the hills and across the valley of Walnut River for about twelve miles.

185

Coming back to Bartlesville we reported our findings to the boss. Upon our recommendation, the greater part of the territory covered by the anticline was leased, and we then sent two surveying parties in charge of J. Russell Crabtree into the area. These men prepared a contour map of the territory covered by the structure. The first wells which we located on this anticline produced gas, and the field later developed into a large gas field with considerable oil.

So far as I know the Augusta Oil and Gas Field was the first in the Mid-Continent area to be surveyed geologically, and for which a contour map was prepared in advance of drilling. Later this method came into general use among oil companies, and before many years the major part of such states as Oklahoma, Kansas, Nebraska, Texas, Missouri, and Arkansas had been surveyed by geologists in the employ of the larger oil companies.

Later plane-table surveys were made on what is now the El Dorado Field north of Augusta. The Doherty interests secured large holdings in this field, and this was the beginning of the Empire Companies which soon became among the most profitable of the Doherty holdings, later merged with the Cities Service Company. The El Dorado and Augusta fields produced a maximum of 90,000 barrels of oil per day.

About this time Doherty was negotiating a bond issue in London to finance the drilling of Kansas holdings, and the bonding company sent to this country two engineers to inspect and evaluate the Doherty properties. I was asked to accompany these men to some gas wells in the northeastern part of the Osage Nation, in Oklahoma. We started out from town in a two-seated surrey. I sat on the front seat with the driver, and the two engineers, sedate, unbending, elderly gentlemen, one of whom wore a monocle and spats, sat behind.

Soon after crossing the Osage line we came to a fence with

a wire gate. One of the engineers adjusted his monocle and stared at the gate.

"My word," he said, "and what might that be?"

"Oh, it's a wire gate," said I.

"A wire gate?" said he. "And pray what is a wire gate?"

"A wire gate," I informed him, "is a gate made of barbed wire."

"Indeed," he exploded, "extraordinary! Barbed wire! I never heard of such a thing! Are there many in America?"

"I've opened ten thousand wire gates," I replied.

"Ten thousand wire gates!" he said. "Most unusual! And how do we get through your bally wire gate?"

I jumped down, opened the gate, and the team and surrey passed through, I closed the gate, hopped back into the surrey and we drove on.

Before long, we came to another fence with a wire gate and I repeated the performance. I heard my Britisher mutter to himself, and he marked something down in his little black book. He kept counting all day long. Every time we came to a gate, he would make a notation in his book. At the end of the day's drive, as we went through the last wire gate, he put his book back in his pocket and I heard him say, "Ten thousand and sixteen wire gates."

After a year and a half, I resigned from the company and Carpenter carried on as head of the geological department. This was one of the first large geological departments in any of the oil companies; at one time, it had over two hundred geologists and plane-table men "hunting structures."

My consulting practice soon increased to such a point that I could not handle it alone, and I became associated with three young men, Joseph M. Perkins, Leslie C. Hanson, and Robert S. Dewey. We also employed from time to time several other young geologists, chiefly as instrument men. Among them were

John L. Ferguson, Robert L. Keyes, and Frank S. Lewis. All of these men, except Hanson, are now engaged in some phase of the oil business.

It was about this time that I first began to hear the term "rock hound." In the popular mind, a rock hound is an individual who wanders around over the hills chasing outcrops of rock, trying to locate an oil field. For a quarter of a century, the term has been current in Oklahoma and other states of the Southwest where oil is produced.

No one knows, for sure, just how or where the term originated; it appears to be one of those things which springs from the soil. One story is that an old farmer in southern Kansas was surprised and concerned to see two men with surveying instruments out on a rocky hill in his pasture. He asked a neighbor if he knew who the intruders were.

"Oh, them's rock hounds," said the neighbor. "They've been chasing that ledge of limestone clean acrost the country. Yesterday Bill Jones, he started to chase 'em off'n his place, but they told him they was huntin' oil, so he let 'em stay. Says he thought if they could locate oil on his farm he'd better let 'em do it."

At any rate, the term is in good repute in the Southwest, being used half humorously to indicate a geologist, and more particularly one engaged in petroleum investigation.

A young "rock hound" is a "pebble pup." This name is applied to young chaps just out of school who are serving their apprenticeship in the field, assisting an older and more experienced geologist. A "rock hound" with his "pebble pup" make up an instrument crew, with plane-table, telescopic alidade, and stadia rod. By this method the greater part of the states of the southern Great Plains were surveyed and many producing oil fields located.

When my stenographer resigned, Nina came into the office

until I could secure another secretary. But she enjoyed the work so much and was so efficient that she remained for more than ten years, in fact until we left the Oklahoma City office for Norman. Lois was then ten years old and Don eight, and both were in school. We secured as housekeeper a very capable woman, Mrs. Maggie Evans, whom the children loved and respected, and who remained with us for several years. During the time when our business was flourishing, Nina looked after the finances, did the bookkeeping, kept lists of leases and properties, and had general charge of the office while the men were in the field.

One of the largest commissions I received during this time was that of attempting to locate a fifty-year fuel supply for one of the large public service corporations of Oklahoma. The general manager of the company had discussed the matter with me several times, and we finally entered into a contract. I was to spend as much time as necessary in scouting eastern Oklahoma, southern Kansas, western Arkansas, and northern Texas in the search for a large and available supply of fuel. Natural gas was preferred, but gas being uncertain, both as to location and as to the life of the field, it was finally decided to spend the greater part of the time in the search for coal.

Certain specifications were handed me. The bed of coal was to be of a certain thickness, not more than a specified distance from a line of railroad, with definite B.T.U. or heating values. The bed should outcrop on the surface at least in part, so that a quantity of coal would be available for strip-pit mining, and, in addition to all other factors, the deposit should be not too far from Oklahoma City.

I employed John L. Ferguson to assist me in this work, outlined the general area to be studied, bought him a Model T Ford car, which was beginning to be used by geologists, and turned him loose, only visiting him occasionally in the field to check his results. Ferguson visited some seventy-five strip-pits. After several months in the field he eliminated all but about ten of these properties. I went into the field with him and after the examination of these ten prospects threw out half. On the remaining five properties, Ferguson prepared maps and made brief preliminary reports which I submitted to the general manager. He spent several days studying these reports and maps, and then called me into consultation. After checking them we both agreed upon a certain area located in Okmulgee County as being the most suitable to the needs of his company.

We drove to Okmulgee County and spent two days in the area. He was satisfied with the proposition and asked me to prepare a complete report. This we did, and presented a fat report of several hundred pages, the largest ever sent out from our office. He paid my bill, and then sent into the area a real estate man, who secured, either by purchase or on long-time options from the landowners, a tract of several thousand acres containing coal. So far as I know this property is still among the assets of the corporation, but it has never been developed.

One of the most interesting and profitable bits of work, and one that brought me much favorable comment, was the discovery of gas in the Texas Panhandle. I had first seen this area in the summer of 1903, at the time we were coming down the Canadian River on a reconnaissance trip for the Reclamation Service. One day, while riding horseback among the breaks of the Canadian twenty miles northeast of Amarillo, I had noticed some outcrops of dolomite ledges among the red beds, and observed that, in some places, these ledges were dipping at rather high angles, suggesting the presence of an anticline.

Two years later, I prepared a report dealing with the geology and water resources of the western part of the Panhandle of Texas. On a map and cross section drawn along the Canadian, I located several anticlines, or domes, and wrote certain paragraphs describing these structures. At this time there was no particular interest attached to anticlines. The relation between geological structure and oil and gas accumulation was suspected by a few geologists, but it was by no means a matter of common knowledge. When I first described the anticlines along the Canadian River, I had no idea that they would ever become commercially valuable, but recorded them as a matter of routine the same as I did other geological phenomena. Having embalmed these anticlines in the literature, I proceeded to forget about them, and it was not until several years later that I had occasion to think of them again.

M. C. Nobles, a wholesale grocer of Amarillo, accompanied by J. T. Moore, one of his traveling salesmen, came to my office in Oklahoma City in 1916 and employed me to go with them to examine a tract of land near Tishomingo, Oklahoma. There Moore had secured a block of oil leases in which he was trying to interest Nobles. I went to Tishomingo with these gentlemen, and, after going over the property, was able to convince them that the chances for oil were very poor. As was natural, they were very much disappointed, but paid my bill without quibbling.

On the way back to Oklahoma City, Mr. Nobles asked me if I knew of any oil or gas prospects near his home in the Panhandle country. At first I said I did not, but happened to remember the anticlines along the Canadian north of Amarillo. So I told him what I had seen when doing work for the government thirteen years before.

He was at once interested and asked all sorts of questions about the location of the structure, its size and character, and my opinion of the chances for oil and gas in that part of the country. I told him that my ideas were somewhat vague, and that about all I knew was that there appeared to be several big anticlines or domes in that region, but that before making any definite recommendations, I would have to go over the ground again. I also said that it would probably be necessary to send a plane-table party into the field and prepare a detailed contour map of the area.

Nobles went home and organized the Amarillo Oil Company, composed of ten businessmen of Amarillo, who each put in one thousand dollars. (This company is reported to have sold out several years later for one million dollars.) I contracted with this company to make a survey of the area and if I found conditions favorable to recommend the location for the drilling of the first well.

In company with one of my associates, Robert S. Dewey, I visited the region and outlined the general area to be surveyed. Mr. Dewey remained and spent six weeks in the field with a plane-table preparing a map. The territory surveyed lay thirty to forty miles northeast of Amarillo on both sides of the Canadian River. The greater part of it was on two large ranches, the Lee Bivins Ranch south of the river, and the R. B. Masterson Ranch to the north. Dewey worked out from the Bivins headquarters at the mouth of Bonita Creek. He secured as rod man an old-time cowboy who was sort of pensioner on the Bivins ranch, who had always worked in the saddle and objected to climbing hills on foot. They rode horseback to and from the work, and for the greater part of the time it was necessary to ford the quicksand of the Canadian, morning and evening.

The map prepared by Dewey showed a large dome, ten to fifteen miles in diameter with a maximum uplift in the center of about four hundred feet, which might well be considered a typical oil-and-gas structure. We named this structure the John Ray Dome, from a prominent butte known as John Ray Butte, located near the western side of the dome. I showed this map to Nobles and his associates, and on my advice the company took oil and gas leases on about 64,000 acres in the vicinity. The greater part of these leases were on lands owned by Bivins and Masterson. For my compensation in outlining this structure, I received one thousand dollars cash, plus all expenses for Dewey and myself, and leases on one-sixteenth of the acreage, or about four thousand acres, which were selected checkerboard fashion throughout the tract secured by the Amarillo Company.

Then came the matter of getting a well drilled to prove or disprove the presence of oil or gas on the property. The company entered into a contract with C. M. Hapgood, a driller of Oklahoma City, to put down a well. Next came the location of the first well. At that time neither oil nor gas had been found within 225 miles of this place. There was then no production in northwest Texas, western Oklahoma, western Kansas, eastern New Mexico, or southeastern Colorado. The nearest oil field was the Electra Field west of Wichita Falls, Texas.

I well remember the occasion of the location of the first well. Accompanied by some half-dozen white-hatted, high-booted ranchmen, and several businessmen of Amarillo, in four automobiles, Dewey and I started out, drove north twenty miles, crossed the Canadian River bridge, then north about ten miles farther to the high prairie. Dewey's map showed that the highest point of the dome appeared to be near John Ray Butte. We picked out the place which, to our minds, appeared as favorable as any; the highest point, structurally, of which we could be certain, and there Dewey and I piled up a little heap of rocks. The cowmen and the Amarillo businessmen were standing around open-eyed, and to them I made a little speech:

"No one knows whether or not the Lord has put any gas or oil in the Panhandle of Texas, but if there should be any oil or gas in this part of the world, this would appear to be the best place to find it. And, because this seems to be a very large dome, it is my judgment that one is more likely to find gas, rather than oil, in the first well drilled on the apex, or high point, of the dome."

One of the cattlemen afterward said to me, "Gould, when you all made that little speech for we alls out there in Masterson's pasture, I couldn't quite decide whether you all was a mighty smart man or a damn bluffer."

They struck gas.

Hapgood drilled the well 2,200 feet deep and encountered several gas-bearing sands, the total amount being about eleven million cubic feet a day. This was the first encountered in the Panhandle of Texas. Later, several other wells were drilled not far away, one of them producing over one hundred million cubic feet a day.

The finding of gas on John Ray Dome stimulated interest in the oil and gas possibilities in other parts of the Panhandle, and I was solicited by owners of other large ranches to work out any possible structures of their properties. The Landergin brothers owned two ranches of approximately one hundred thousand acres each, west of Amarillo. We ran plane-table surveys on these properties and located two structures on each ranch. The Amarillo Oil Company leased the Bravo Ranch north of the Canadian on the New Mexico line and we made a plane-table survey showing a well-marked anticline, which we called the Bravo Dome. This was one of the anticlines which I had mapped and published in Water Supply Paper Number 191, many years before. We also mapped structures on the Herring and Bivins ranches northwest of Amarillo. All of these structures were afterward drilled, but none of them secured profitable production.

One structure which we discovered was located near the station Cliffside, a few miles northwest of Amarillo. This we mapped and named the Cliffside Dome. Some years later this was drilled and large deposits of helium gas were encountered.

It is the gas from this dome which supplies the government helium plant near Amarillo, the largest of its kind in the world.

For several years we had an office at Amarillo with Robert S. Dewey in charge of several instrument men. Our policy in making plane-table surveys of the various properties was the same as at John Ray Dome; namely, first, we received all expenses for making the survey, next, we took a substantial sum in cash, usually five hundred or one thousand dollars, depending on the size of the area, and lastly, we received oil and gas leases on a certain percentage of the land. In other words, from each project we first took care of our overhead, then assured ourselves of some profit, and for the remainder we were willing to gamble with the land owner. Because, as we well knew and as we always told our clients, the business of prospecting for oil or gas was first, last, and all the time a gamble. No one knows in advance of drilling what will be found at any particular place. There is always a risk in drilling for oil and all the geologist can do is to minimize that risk.

Perhaps I should say that we followed this plan in every case but one. We surveyed eight structures in the area along the breaks of the Canadian on which we followed the plan as outlined above. But on the ninth structure, try as we might, we were not able to secure any acreage. These were the circumstances:

Mr. Burk Burnett of Fort Worth owned a block containing one hundred square miles, located north of Panhandle, the county seat of Carson County. This was the same man for whom the town of Burkburnett near Wichita Falls was named. The cattle brand for his Panhandle ranch was 6666. There was a Panhandle legend to the effect that he won the ranch in a poker game when he was lucky enough to hold four sixes.

Three businessmen of Amarillo went to Fort Worth and made a deal with Burk Burnett for prospecting for oil and gas on the

6666 ranch. E. S. Blaisdell, the prime mover in the project, came to me to negotiate for our services in surveying the property. We drove over the ranch and I was able to see indications of a large structure, the apex of which lay within about two miles of the north line of the ranch, and I recommended that a plane-table survey be made.

He was willing that this be done, but when I suggested my usual terms, namely overhead, cash, and acreage, he objected and said that he and his partners had agreed not to part with any of the acreage. So we compromised on a higher per diem for the surveys and a larger amount of cash than usual. We put two parties in the field, and they spent several weeks with plane-table, making the map. When completed, it showed a well-marked dome, which we named the 6666 dome. The apex of the dome lay near the north edge of the one-hundred-square-mile block and extended thence for several miles north across other properties and to the Canadian River.

Now for the irony of fate. Talk about luck! Luck does enter into many matters of human endeavor. We had secured acreage as part pay for our work on eight of the nine domes which we surveyed in the Panhandle. But the 6666 dome, on which we were not able to secure acreage, was the first of the nine to produce large quantities of oil. The world-famous Borger Oil Field is located on the north slope of this dome, but not on the Burk Burnett Ranch.

The drilling of the many wells in the Panhandle of Texas, following the discovery of oil and gas brought out one fact of great scientific interest, namely, the presence of a buried granite ridge. In a paper published several years later, I named this buried ridge the "Amarillo Mountains." It appears to be an extension to the northwest of the Wichita Mountains of southwestern Oklahoma. The series of oil and gas fields located along this granite ridge, referred to as the Amarillo or Panhandle Field, has become one of the major gas fields of the United States.

It is as a gas field that the Panhandle country is chiefly famous. The area producing natural gas has been found to extend north across the Panhandle of Oklahoma into Kansas, and contains some 2,500,000 acres. Many wells have produced over one hundred million cubic feet of gas each day, and there are several thousand gas wells in that area. At one time, engineers estimated the total gas reserves of the Amarillo region at 15,000,000,000,000 (fifteen trillion) cubic feet. The life of the field has been estimated to be over forty years. Gas from this field is piped to Denver, Indianapolis, Chicago, Omaha, Minneapolis, Kansas City, Wichita, and Dallas.

Amarillo has grown from a prairie cow town of a few thousand people to a modern city of 70,000. Scores of smaller towns have sprung up in the oil fields and many towns have increased their population several times. All of this started from the observation of a lone government geologist riding horseback among the breaks of the Canadian River in 1903.

It was in the late summer of 1919 while I was doing geological work on the High Plains that I witnessed the birth of a storm.

One afternoon I was tracing formations on the Landergin Ranch some eighty miles west of Amarillo. The day had been warm and sultry, with little wind and scarcely a cloud in the sky. About two o'clock I noticed a small, light-colored cloud forming about twenty-five miles to the north. In half an hour the cloud had increased in size, and still later I saw a flash of lightning. As I kept watching the cloud, it became darker and larger, and soon spread over the northern sky.

About four o'clock I started east toward Amarillo. By this time I could see in the northwest a black cloud, and frequent flashes of lightning, and hear the thunder. The storm, with a heavy downpour of rain, chased me into Amarillo and passed on eastward.

The next day's Oklahoma City newspapers reported a storm in Oklahoma. As a matter of curiosity, I sent for the Little Rock and Memphis newspapers and was able to trace the storm, which I had seen born, from the Panhandle across Oklahoma and Arkansas and into Tennessee.

Several of my investigations were in west central Texas. In the work of this region I was associated for the most part with Charles F. Colcord of Oklahoma City. I had known Mr. Colcord for many years, first becoming acquainted with him in 1900, soon after coming to Oklahoma.

Colcord had among his friends C. U. Connellee of Eastland, Texas, both men coming from the blue-grass region of Kentucky. Colcord and I went to Eastland, and the three of us spent a number of days driving over the country scouting for oil possibilities. He returned home but I secured a horse and buggy and for several weeks continued my study of geological conditions in northern Eastland, eastern Stephens, and southern Young counties.

I found several localities that looked fairly promising, some of which have since become productive oil fields, but the one which showed the best surface indications was located near the little hamlet of South Bend at the forks of the Brazos River in southern Young County. At this place I found some rock ledges dipping in such a manner that I suspected the location of an anticline which might develop into a profitable oil field.

I returned to Oklahoma City, told Colcord what I had found, and he and Connellee visited the region with me. Connellee, being a cattle man and speaking the language of the land owners, remained there for a time and took leases on several thousand acres of land which later developed into the South Bend Oil Field.

We had been fighting our way through the catclaw and mesquite brush near South Bend, jumping gullies and scrambling up and sliding down shale banks. Just before noon, hot and dirty, we came out on top of a small knoll overlooking the fertile valley of Brazos River and sat down on a ledge of sandstone to rest.

Scattered over the surface we had noticed evidences of prehistoric workshops. There were flint concretions, sometimes whole, but more often broken; also a number of rejects, or incomplete flint implements, and many flakes and fragments that had been broken off in the process of shaping the implements.

As we sat there on the sandstone ledge, with our feet hanging over, we began speculating as to the manner of men who had fashioned the implements we were finding. Were they Indians like the Comanches, who lived in the country when the white man came, or were they a prehistoric people whose record had been lost? On the slope below the ledge I saw a cluster of flint flakes, and a good specimen of a reject, and jumped off the ledge to pick it up. Standing on the slope below, with my head about on a level with my companion's feet, I saw a little natural rock shelf on the under side of the sandstone ledge, and reaching back, I picked up two perfect arrowheads.

Some old Indian perhaps five hundred or one thousand years ago (who knows?) had sat where we were sitting, and by knocking together two flint concretions had chipped off the flakes which we found lying on the slope. When he had shaped two arrow points to his liking, he had laid them for safe keeping on the shelf, where they had remained until an oil geologist happened to pick them up. Why had he not reclaimed his property? Had he forgotten them? Had he lost the place? Or had an enemy crawled over the clay banks through the catclaw and mesquite?

I had been sent by Colcord to check on a few thousand acres

of ranch land near Langtry, Texas, in order to determine whether there were any anticlines or other favorable showings of oil structures.

Langtry is a little town of one store, one post office, one railroad depot, three white families, six to ten Mexican families, and one street of about the same length, located near the mouth of the Pecos River. This is the town made famous by Judge Roy Bean and his "law west of the Pecos."

This happened during the time when the followers of Villa and of Carranza were enjoying their favorite summer pastime of pot-shooting each other from behind mesquite bushes. If one left the little village of Langtry and walked a few hundred yards down to the edge of the cliff overlooking the Rio Grande, he might see on the Mexico side of the river a camp of Carranzistas, while a few miles upstream a body of Villistas were camped. At the town there was a detachment of United States soldiers, a corporal and five privates, whose duty it was to patrol some fifty miles of the river and prevent the warring Mexican factions from crossing to our side. But in spite of the patrol, members of both factions did cross frequently, chiefly under cover of darkness, in order to buy tobacco and other necessities at the Langtry store.

One day I had a scare. I had climbed down the steep cliff bordering the Rio Grande and was working my way upstream on the sandbar near the water's edge, studying the outcrops and looking for fossils. Suddenly, on rounding a little bend and stepping out from behind the willows, I saw directly across the river some eight or ten villainous-looking Mexicans, squatting and lying on the sand, each with a rifle and belt of cartridges. They looked at me and I looked at them. They made no contribution to the conversation. I knew no Spanish except, "*Buenos dias, Señores.*" This expression of good feeling on my part brought no response from them, so I kept on ambling upstream. I will admit to a creepy, crawly feeling up and down my spine when I was obliged to turn my back on them.

A few days later, the ranch owner, his son, and I were riding horses and made noon stop at a water hole near the railroad to build a fire and toast our bacon on sticks over mesquite coals. Following the custom of the country, the other two men each had a Winchester strapped to his saddle. While we were eating our lunch, a Southern Pacific train passed going east, and we noticed that all the passengers were craning their necks out of the window to get a view of us.

Next day, when we got the San Antonio newspapers, scare headlines announced the startling news that a party of Mexicans "heavily armed" had crossed the Rio Grande near Langtry and were preparing to devastate the town.

And so I learned about news reports from the seat of war.

At the entry of the United States in the World War, the young men with me enlisted for service. Dewey and Hanson took training and became lieutenants, Dewey spending some months in France, Hanson remaining at Camp Travis in Texas. Ferguson was top sergeant in the San Mihiel drive. Perkins was in the naval service at the Great Lakes Training School. I offered my services to the Government and was enrolled as expert on mineral resources, but was never called.

While the young men were in service, Nina and I carried on as best we could. We kept the office going and accepted a number of commissions for work in the field. Frank S. Lewis helped us at the time. During the three years following the close of the World War, the price of oil was abnormally high, reaching at one time $3.50 per barrel. Many geologists entered the oil game, and hundreds of young men took training in universities to fit themselves for the profession.

During these years the scope of our work expanded. At one time in addition to the main office at Oklahoma City, we had branch offices at Amarillo, with Dewey in charge; at Fort Worth, with Hanson in charge; and at Kansas City. At one time we also maintained an office at Owensboro, Kentucky. Nina, Perkins, and I maintained headquarters at Oklahoma City, but each of us frequently visited the other offices to check on the work.

It was necessary to employ several men to assist in the detail work. In addition to Ferguson, Lewis, and Keyes, who were the stand-bys, the following men were in our employ: Carl Horn, Fred Brasted, Everett Osborne, John Toberman, Francis Mulky, Phil Blackwelder, and Sidney Packard. My files show that between the years 1911 and 1924 I conducted examinations and prepared reports on 572 different properties.

The high price of oil was followed by a slump in prices. By this time the greater number of the large oil companies had organized their own geological staffs and the demand for our services declined. In 1922 our organization disbanded. Nina and I retained the office at Oklahoma City until July 1, 1924.

In many ways I enjoyed my venture into the business world, but in other ways some of the experiences were anything but pleasant. My training had been largely academic and scientific, and it was a new experience to go up against the hard realities of business as it is practiced in this country. It took some time for me to adjust my thinking, and to realize that in business one must always be on guard, must always watch the other fellow, to see that he does not secure an undue advantage.

In work such as ours, one meets all sorts of characters. We used to classify the people who came to our offices as follows: first, businessmen; second, promoters; third, shysters; fourth, plain thieves.

And it is not always easy to distinguish between these classes of individuals. Businessmen are, as a rule, not difficult to deal with. It is a joy to be associated with men like M. C. Nobles,

C. F. Colcord, or C. U. Connellee. Men of this type know what they want, expect and appreciate honest service, and are willing to pay for it. They take the chances of trade as they come. If they make money out of a deal, they give credit where credit is due, and if they lose they come up smiling and hope for better luck next time.

Promoters are of many kinds. A few of them are honest but poor, but many of them are dishonest and oppulent. I believe I have known all kinds, starting with the fellows who used to hang around Oklahoma City at the time of the first boom in 1908–10, up to the different gangs that infested the same city after the Oklahoma City oil field was developed in 1929–31. A few of them overstepped themselves and landed in the federal penitentiary, but the greater number were shrewd enough to escape.

These gentry used to wear out our office furniture. In some instances, in the early days of my business experience, they were so thoroughly disguised as businessmen that we were deceived and entered into contracts with them and spent time and money in surveying properties and writing reports. If the report happened to be favorable, the promoter would sometimes pay for it, then go out and organize a company and exploit my name. If the report was unfavorable, he would refuse to pay, and we were left "holding the sack."

I remember a case in Kansas City where a certain promoter, who used as many initials as there were letters in his surname, engaged me to do a piece of work. I was not able to find any favorable indications of oil on his property, and when my report was submitted, the promoter refused to pay for it, saying that such a report would not help him sell stock. I was obliged to sue for my bill, but never collected the money. This gentleman afterwards promoted a company in another state, using as sucker bait the name of a notorious American explorer. Both men later served time in the federal penitentiary. The promoter next showed up at Oklahoma City and repeated the performance, and was again indicted by the federal grand jury.

We were usually able to recognize shysters and to steer clear of them. These are the individuals who like to hang around the office, to "get an earful," catch stray scraps of information, and go out and peddle it. We had our experiences with this class of individuals, but so far as I know, suffered no particular ill effects.

With the plain thieves, it was different. These were the men who either stole information or who deliberately misrepresented facts. In one case a man for whom I wrote a report discarded entirely the last sheet of the report and substituted one of his own, in which the conclusions and recommendations were entirely different from those I had written, and forged my name at the bottom. After this experience, as a matter of self-protection, I was obliged to use for reports paper with my name and address printed on each sheet.

CHAPTER 9

SECOND TERM
AS STATE GEOLOGIST

DURING THE THIRTEEN YEARS I was engaged in business, the Oklahoma Geological Survey carried on. I have already said that on my resignation Dr. Ohern was appointed
director. After a little more than two years, he and Frank
Buttram, the chemist for the Survey, resigned to join with some
Oklahoma City businessmen to form an oil company which
prospered, and both men became wealthy.

C. W. Shannon, who had been field geologist for the Survey,
was appointed director in 1914 and continued to serve until
April, 1923. From year to year the appropriations by the legislature had been increased. In 1919 a new Geology Building was
erected on the campus, in which the survey had ample quarters
for offices, laboratories, and library.

At the time of one of the political upheavals in Oklahoma a
man was elected governor who knew nothing of economics,
little of government, and less of administration. He was motivated largely by impulse, egotism, and love of display. The
fact that he was soon impeached did not prevent him from
doing much harm to Oklahoma during the short time he remained in office. Among other things detrimental to the state,
he vetoed the appropriations for the Geological Survey. His ex-
cuse was that the well-log bureau, formerly administered by the

survey, had been transferred to the Corporation Commission, and that, therefore, there was no further need for the survey.

Charles E. Decker, professor of paleontology at the University, was appointed custodian of the survey property, and for more than a year he very effectively carried on the work. Survey Bulletin 32, entitled, *Geology of the Southern Ouachita Mountains of Oklahoma,* was published during this time. Charles W. Honess had prepared this bulletin after spending the three field seasons of 1917, 1918, and 1919 in the area. Many geologists consider this report one of the finest pieces of scientific writing ever published in Oklahoma.

There has always been considerable confusion in the popular mind about the proper pronunciation of the names Ouachita and Washita—names which are applied to certain geographic entities in Louisiana, Arkansas, and Oklahoma. The names are pronounced exactly alike, Wash-e-taw, the accent is on the first syllable. Ouachita is the French spelling, and Washita the English.

Perhaps a word of explanation regarding the origin of the names and of the spelling might aid in clarifying the subject. During the sixteenth century French explorers, traders, and trappers from New Orleans ascended the Mississippi and many of its tributaries. They were often accompanied, as guides, by Choctaw Indians who lived in what is now the state of Mississippi.

As they ascended Red River, they encountered a tributary entering from the north which their Choctaw guides called *Owa Chito,* explaining it was from two Choctaw words, *Owa,* meaning hunt, and *Chito,* meaning big. The name meant "big hunt," and was so called because Choctaw hunters, crossing the Mississippi, found many buffalo along this stream, and once a year went on their *Owa Chito,* their big hunt, or the hunt far away from home, to secure their winter's meat. The Frenchmen gallicized the spelling and the pronunciation of the name, so that the river tributary to the Red was named Ouachita River. Sometime later the mountains located in what is now southwestern Arkansas and southeastern Oklahoma, in which this river took its rise, became the Ouachita Mountains. This form of spelling has been preserved in Arkansas and Louisiana, so that today in Arkansas, in addition to Ouachita River and Ouachita Mountains, there is a town Ouachita, also Ouachita County, Ouachita College, and several Ouachita townships. The Ouachita River flows from Arkansas across northeastern Louisiana, and in that state there is a Ouachita parish and town.

As the Frenchmen explored farther and farther west up Red River, they found a number of tributary streams, and finally, one larger than the others emptying from the north, which the Choctaws also called *Owa Chito,* explaining that they had found many buffalo along this stream. To this river the Frenchmen gave the name *Faux* (false) Ouachita. This spelling appears on some of the earlier maps of the region.

Later the prefix *Faux* was dropped, and soon thereafter, when English-speaking people entered the region, the spelling of the word was anglicized, so that the name of this river is now spelled Washita, this being the English spelling of the original Indian name. In Oklahoma there is a Washita County, also a town, and several townships named Washita.

The mountains in southeastern Oklahoma and southwestern Arkansas, to which geographers and geologists apply the name Ouachita, are about two hundred miles long, averaging fifty miles in width and extend from Little Rock, Arkansas, westward to Atoka, Oklahoma. The group as a whole consists of several parallel barrier ridges or ranges, all heavily timbered, which in Arkansas trend east and west, but in Oklahoma become arcuate and bend to the southwest. They are held up by a bed of massive sandstone, the Jackfork sandstone, which averages five thousand feet in thickness.

Studies by geologists have shown that these ridges have been formed as a result of a series of extensive thrust faults. Great slices of the earth's crust have been shoved up from the south, one over the other, something like shingles on a roof, so that the region has been foreshortened many miles. In this regard, the Ouachitas resemble the Alps, which are believed to have been carried for considerable distances by thrust faulting.

In Oklahoma these barrier ridges which make up the Ouachita group have received local names, such as Pine, Winding Stair, Jack Fork, Kiamichi, Buffalo, and Rich. In Arkansas the names Fourch, Black Fork, Crystal, Caddo Gap, Mazern, Blue, and Cossatot are applied to individual mountain ranges.

In Oklahoma the popular name for these mountains is not Ouachita, but Kiamichi. Notwithstanding the fact that Kiamichi is, strictly speaking, the name of but one of several ranges in the Ouachita group, this name is ordinarily applied to the mountains as a whole. One speaks of going camping in the Kiamichis, or of taking a fishing trip down in the Kiamichi country. Sometimes the name is even shortened to Kiamish. Rarely is Ouachita used in Oklahoma except by geologists.

I have been told that in Arkansas the popular name for these mountains is Ozarks, and that the part of the true Ozark Mountains of Missouri which spills over into northern Arkansas is called the Boston Mountains.

So the geographers and geologists seem to be fighting a losing battle in attempting to teach the people of Oklahoma and Arkansas to use the name Ouachita. What the final outcome may be no one can tell. Very probably the natives of Arkansas will continue to use the name Ozarks, and those of Oklahoma will still speak of the Kiamichi country, while the scientist, conscious of his own rectitude, will continue to be highbrow and use the name Ouachita.

But regardless of the pronunciation of the name, the fact remains that in many ways this Ouachita Mountain country is as different from the greater part of the rest of the state as daylight is from dark. It is unfortunate that very few people in Oklahoma have ever seen it.

A few years ago, during the first week in May, Mr. and Mrs. Carl Williams and Nina and I, drove thirty miles through the forest over the highway leading from Broken Bow to Bethel. What a revelation! How different from the Oklahoma to which most of us have been accustomed!

This road penetrates the edge of a pine forest so large that in it one might lose the state of Rhode Island. This is not a country of broad views and unobscured vision, like most parts of the state; rather is it a region of tantalizing glimpses and long vistas. As far as the eye can carry one sees rank upon rank of tall, straight trunks of oak and pine rising from the earth to support a canopy of green. Through this canopy one catches fleeting glimpses of blue sky and fleecy clouds, with shafts of golden sunlight streaming through. Along the valleys are clumps of birch and sweet gum, of maple and ash. The flowering dogwood in full bloom stands like sheeted ghosts among the trees.

Red honeysuckle climbs the bushes. Roadside violets immodestly wink blue eyes at sweet William. May apples and Solomon's seal cluster among the brush. Water lilies float on the ponds. Redbud blushes pink and tries to hide among the trees. All our old flower friends are there, and a dozen new ones patiently waiting an introduction. Every little while a tiny creek crosses the road, with water crystal-clear babbling over the stones, chuckling through the rushes, tinkling like fairy anvils over mimic waterfalls.

And the road, the open road, now straight as an arrow, tree-lined, converging to a vanishing point in the distance; now winding in graceful, hairpin curves back and forth along the mountain side. The delightful surprises waiting just around the next bend give added joy to each mile.

Here and there one passes an old clearing in the forest, the remainder of a once happy home. Here is a deserted log cabin, with clapboard roof, a stable, and a few scrubby, tangled, half-dead apple trees, and there are the deserted fields, gully-washed, with rotting rail fences, growing up to broom grass and sassafras. A sagging picket fence with a patch of yellow wild mustard shows where there was once a garden. What hopes and fears, what joys and sorrows, what successes and disappointments once mingled here. Every deserted house, every abandoned farm represents a tragedy.

New farms are being opened in the forest; trees being murdered, condemned by girdling to a lingering death. Men with one mule hitched to a shovel plow are working among the stumps. Hound dogs and razorbacks loaf in the yards. New log cabins with stick chimneys and fresh clapboard roofs; with split rail fences around the fields, and picket fences riven from oak, around the garden. Wagons are loaded with cross ties and lumber. Here and there a sawmill with its piles of logs, stacks of new-sawn lumber, and a sawdust pile. Little two-roomed box houses near the mill, with tow-headed children playing in the yard, and a woman with a baby in her arms standing in the doorway.

These are not big mountains. The big ones, the Kiamichis, lie miles away to the north, and from the hill tops we can occasionally catch a glimpse of the tree-covered mountain barrier stretching to the east and west as far as the eye can see. These are little friendly hills that cuddle down and talk to us. They laugh at us and we laugh back.

Cardinals flashing like glints of red fire in the bushes by the streams call "Cheer, cheer, cheer." Woodpeckers drum on dead pines. Mocking birds carol. Blue jays flit among the trees. James Whitcomb Riley was right when he said:

*"Mister blue jay full o' sass
In them baseball clothes o' his
Struts 'round just like he owned the premises."*

And the rocks! Shales and sandstones and cherts and novaculites, twisted, faulted, contorted, standing on edge, and overturned, bleak reminders of the torturing torment of the time when the world was new.

Surely the old Hebrew prophet had some such place as this in mind when, three thousand years ago, he wrote, "And all the trees of the hills shall clap their hands."

But we were talking about the Geological Survey. In 1923, a special session of the legislature changed the governing body of the survey. By the provisions of the new law the Geological Survey Commission was abolished and the survey was placed under the control of the Board of Regents of the University. Some four years later the Board of Regents, by resolution, placed the executive control of the survey under the president of the University and specified that the director of the survey should rank as a dean.

When the members of the Board of Regents found themselves with a new "child" on their hands, they "passed the buck" to Frank Buttram, a member of the board, a geologist, who had formerly been on the survey staff. As one member afterward said, "None of the rest of the board knows anything about a geological survey, and Frank was supposed to know everything about one." And, so, by resolution, the matter of securing a director and rehabilitating the survey was left to Mr. Buttram.

A few days later, he called a meeting of some thirty geologists in his office at Oklahoma City. There were representatives from geological societies at Tulsa, Oklahoma City, Okmulgee, Ardmore, and Ponca City, besides several men from the University, including J. S. Buchanan, then the acting president, and V. E. Monnett and C. E. Decker, from the Department of Geology. From Oklahoma City were D. W. Ohern, J. B. Umpleby, and Irving Perrine, all of whom had formerly been connected with the department. I was asked to be present.

We spent half a day in Buttram's office canvassing the situation. The most important matter was the selection of a director for the survey. After going quite fully into the matter and discussing several names, we all agreed that the best man for the position was Hugh D. Miser. He was a graduate of the University of Arkansas, had been assistant state geologist of Tennessee, and for several years had been connected with the U. S. Geological Survey. He was well acquainted with the geology of Oklahoma, having compiled the geological map of the state, which at that time was in the process of publication, and he was very popular with all geologists.

Buttram appointed Ohern, Umpleby, and me as a committee to draft two telegrams, one to Miser, the other to the director of the U. S. Geological Survey, offering Miser the position as director of the Oklahoma Survey.

The next morning I happened to be in Buttram's office when Miser's reply came. He declined the offer, preferring to remain in government service. Buttram and I looked at each other across the desk, both obviously thinking the same thing. What to do? The man who had been the unanimous choice of the leading geologists of the state for the directorship had refused to accept the position. We sat there for several minutes, each busy with his own thoughts, and revolving in our minds the next best man for the job.

Suddenly, Buttram said with a sigh, "I wish to goodness, Gould, you would take the place."

"But, why, Frank?" I said. "I've had it once. I have my own business well established, plenty to do, my home and my friends in Oklahoma City. Why should I go back to the survey, get under the load, and do it all over again?"

Buttram straightened himself in his chair, looked me straight in the eye, and said:

"I'll tell you exactly why; because the Geological Survey is your baby; because you were at the borning of the thing; because you nursed it through its childhood, fought its battles, and licked its enemies. The child is in a bad way; it's been decapitated and needs a new head. Go back, Gould, and resuscitate it."

"Those are mighty big words, Frank," I replied. "I'm not sure that I know just what they all mean. But really, I'm honest when I say that I do not want the job."

"Think it over," he said. "Go home and talk to Nina. I'll bet she'd like to go back to Norman."

And so I did. When I went home at noon, I said, "Nina, how would you like to be the wife of the director of the Oklahoma Geological Survey once more?"

"Why, what do you mean?" she said.

And so I told her of Miser's refusal and of Buttram's suggestion that I take over the survey. We talked over the whole situation. There were so many factors involved that it was not easy to arrive at a decision. We had been happy in our work and with our associates in Oklahoma City. Nina had her clubs and societies; she had been state president of the Business and Professional Women's Clubs, and had a state-wide acquaintance. She had worked in community fund drives in Oklahoma City, and for some months had been acting superintendent of the fund. She was frequently called upon by the Chamber of

Commerce to aid in putting on membership drives and to help at conventions. All of these things she very much enjoyed, and at them she was tremendously efficient.

I belonged to Rotary, Men's Dinner Club, Chamber of Commerce, and other local organizations, and had taken a leading part in various activities. We both had many friends among both business and professional men and women, not only of Oklahoma City, but of the entire state.

On the other hand, we had been very happy when we had lived at Norman. We had been married at Norman, and there our children had been born. Some of the best friends we had in the world were connected with the University. Neither of us enjoyed living in a large city. I always will be a country boy who likes to twiddle his toes in the dirt. Oklahoma City then had a population of 150,000 people, was growing rapidly, and each year the noise and bustle and confusion were becoming more and more distasteful to us.

The thing that finally decided us to accept the offer and go back to the treadmill of the survey was the fact that both Lois and Don were ready to enter the University. We knew that for at least five years one or both of them would be in school in Norman. Like most parents, we preferred to have the children with us as long as possible. So, next day, Nina and I went down to Buttram's office and had a heart-to-heart talk with him. We could do this frankly because we were friends of long standing. Buttram's wife, Merle Newby, had been in high school with Nina at Guthrie, and we had been together at Norman and Oklahoma City for many years.

Finally we made this proposition to Frank: I would take over the administration of the survey on three conditions. First, he was to sound out the leading geologists of the state and find if they were agreeable to my appointment. Second, I was to be permitted to close up the loose ends of my private business. And third, I was to be allowed to take my usual summer vacations in Colorado.

To all of these he agreed. He got in touch by letter or telephone with various geologists over the state, and later he told me that the sentiment seemed unanimous that I should take over the survey. So he wrote an official letter appointing me director of the survey. This appointment I accepted.

On July 1, 1924, I took my place for the second time at the desk of the director of the Oklahoma Geological Survey. This was twenty-four years after I had first come to the University of Oklahoma to organize the Department of Geology; sixteen years after I had organized the survey; and thirteen years after I had resigned the directorship to enter business.

During these years many changes had taken place. Both the state and the University had made rapid strides. In spite of a horde of self-seeking politicians, who, like the poor, are always with us, Oklahoma had developed rapidly.

When I came to Norman in 1900, the town had a population of possibly 2,000 people; the University consisted of a single building on a forty-acre campus, with the little elm trees scarcely higher than one's head; the faculty had seven members, and the entire student body was about 350, mostly in preparatory work. There were sixty college students.

When I returned in 1924, Norman had perhaps 9,000 inhabitants; there were twenty impressive buildings in shady groves on a 120-acre campus, with a faculty of 300 and a student body of more than 4,000. In 1924 the Department of Geology had twenty times as many students as there had been college students on the campus when I came. To say it differently, in 1924 there was an enrollment of about 1,200 in geology, as against sixty college students in 1900. This is a very remarkable, a very wonderful thing that my eyes have seen. The like will probably never occur again, for it is doubtful that the occasion will ever again arise that could produce such results.

During the thirteen years, there had been a number of changes in the Department of Geology. Charles H. Taylor, Irving Perrine, and Alex McCoy, all of whom had taught in the department, had resigned to enter business. M. G. Mehl, who was head of the department for a short time, was teaching at the University of Missouri. For one year, Willis T. Lee of the U. S. Geological Survey had been head, but the routine of administration irked him and he went back to the work he enjoyed with the federal survey. J. B. Umpleby was head of the department for several years but had resigned to enter business.

So that during the decade between 1914 and 1924 the academic mortality rate in the department had been high. This was due largely to the fact that it was during that period that the science of oil geology began to come into its own in the business world. The rapid development of the petroleum industry and the fact that petroleum executives had learned that the geologist might minimize the risk in drilling oil wells were largely responsible for this rapid turnover.

Nor can the geologist be censured. When an underpaid college professor is offered a salary double or treble that which he is receiving as a teacher to go with an oil or a mining company, it is only natural that he should accept. Fortunately, however, there will always be the faithful few who are willing to remain, men who are in love with the work, who find ample compensation in results obtained, and who have learned that happiness consists "not in things that a man possesseth."

I found on the campus of the University one of the most efficient geological departments in any university in the United States. In many schools, not only in geology, but in other departments as well, there is often one eminent man with a nationwide, or even world-wide, reputation, surrounded by a group of more or less mediocre satellites who shine largely in reflected glory. Not so at Oklahoma in 1924. There were nine men of somewhat equal ability, all excellent teachers or research men. The men in the department, with the specialty of each, were as follows: V. E. Monnett, head of the department, structural geology; Charles E. Decker, paleontology; Samuel Weidman, petrography; A. J. Williams, physiography; G. E. Anderson, sedimentation; C. J. Bollinger, geography; O. F. Evans, meteorology; R. A. Wilson, stratigraphy; J. T. Lonsdale, mineralogy.

In addition there were in the department several instructors who taught classes in elementary geology. Of these I now remember C. L. Cooper, J. A. Stone, Ray Six, George Wood, and H. A. Ireland. Professor Wilson resigned and his place has been taken by F. A. Melton. Lonsdale also resigned and his place in mineralogy has been taken by C. A. Merritt. For several years Ray Six was head of the Department of Geology at Oklahoma A. and M. College. Others have resigned from time to time. J. Willis Stovall[1] teaches invertebrate paleontology, and E. L. Lucas now teaches mineralogy. Anderson and Weidman have passed away.

The School of Petroleum Engineering was added to the College of Engineering and H. C. George was made head. He proved to be a most efficient man, a good executive, a splendid teacher, and a man who attracted students. The new school grew rapidly and for many years it has been considered one of the best schools of petroleum engineering in the United States.

I found things in the survey much disorganized. The department had been cramped for room, and when the activities of the survey were discontinued, their rooms were appropriated by the department for offices, lecture rooms, and laboratories. Gradually this matter adjusted itself.

[1] Since deceased.—Ed.

My first assistant was Mrs. Bess Mills-Bullard. For several years she had been a member of the staff under Shannon, and was of great assistance in getting started again. As secretary I secured John S. Redfield, who proved to be invaluable. Both Mrs. Bullard and Mr. Redfield threw themselves wholeheartedly into the work, and they made a good team. Mrs. Bullard remained for two summers, and Mr. Redfield continued until 1931.

The principal work of a state geological survey is to find out all that is to be known about the geology and the mineral wealth of a state and to tell the world about it. The work is partly scientific and partly economic, but the scientific investigation must always precede economic development. It is necessary to know the rock strata, their thickness and extent, and what the rocks contain, before any permanent or lasting work can be done on the development of the economic products contained in these beds. This is particularly true of the non-metallic minerals, such as clay, shale, stone, Portland cement rock, gypsum, salt, and glass sand, all of which are so abundant in Oklahoma.

Unfortunately, neither the general public nor the politicians understand these things. In order to receive appropriations, on which to exist, and to do work of value to the people of a state, a geological survey must ever be receptive to popular demand. However much the man at the head of the survey would prefer to do strictly scientific work, he is rarely permitted to do so. In order to exist, a survey must continually pour out a stream of bulletins decorated on the front page with the name of some mineral. The head of the survey must stress, at least on the title page, some such thing as coal, oil, zinc, clay, or stone, and, if he can manage to slip in the results of some scientific investigation, geology is just so much to the good, and his brother scientists will rise up and call him blessed. For, be it known, geological formations are no respecters of state lines or other political boundaries. The rocks which outcrop along the Rocky Mountain front, or along the valley of the upper Mississippi River are of tremendous importance in the interpretation of geological conditions in Kansas and Oklahoma. The Scriptures say: "No man liveth unto himself." We might well paraphrase and say that, "Geologically, no state lives unto itself."

These considerations, the results of over thirty years' experience, influenced me in shaping the policies of the survey. I endeavored to publish as much as possible. My motto was: "Get as much geological information as possible to as many people as possible, in the shortest possible time, at the lowest possible cost."

I found a number of manuscripts awaiting publication. Some of them were nearly complete, others were in such a state that it was not feasible to attempt to publish them. This is one of the misfortunes of political interference with scientific work. The lost motion, the cessation of activity, the loss of the interest on the investment which the state had made. The lack of continuity of service. No one knows how many thousands of dollars had been spent in the preparation of these manuscripts. But on account of gubernatorial ignorance and incompetence, the work was interrupted before completion, the authors scattered to other employment, and the work of years and the money spent on the reports went into the scrap heap.

The work of the director of a state survey is not easy. There are a thousand and one things to be done. He must shape policies, decide on what reports should be published, and see that the manuscripts are prepared and printed. He must answer numerous letters on all sorts of subjects. He must interview a great variety of individuals, from the dear lady who thinks the state geologist can stop all his other work and find oil on her land; and the suave promoter who wears out the office furniture because he needs to use the geologist's name to put across some shady deal; all the way to old miners, bleary-eyed and trembling, who unwrap on his desk chunks of rock that they are certain contain gold, but which usually prove to be iron pyrite. There is a constant stream of callers, as well as a deluge of letters on all sorts of subjects.

The director must always be on the alert to distinguish between private work and public work. It is his business to serve all the people of the state and do everything in his power to develop its mineral wealth. But in so doing he must be extremely wary that no private individuals use the name of the survey in order to secure an undue advantage. But be as careful as he may, he is often subject to criticism.

I began my work by publishing such manuscripts as I found on file. There were two county reports ready for printing, namely, *Geology of Cimarron County*, by E. P. Rothrock, and *Geology of Love County*, by Fred E. Bullard. These were published as Bulletins 33 and 34.

During the time the survey was quiescent, with no funds available, and with Dr. Decker as custodian, the geologists of Oklahoma under the direction of Sidney Powers had arranged with the U. S. Geological Survey for the publication of a colored geological map of the state. This map was greatly needed, and had been one of the projects I had in mind on the organization of the survey in 1900. H. D. Miser of the federal survey came to Oklahoma and spent a good part of a year's time on the work. Being a government man, he had access to the confidential files of various oil companies which might not have been opened to a state man. In the compilation of data, Miser consulted more than one thousand such maps, and was thus able to secure a large amount of information otherwise unobtainable.

When I took over the direction of the survey I found that the first draft of this map was nearing completion in Miser's office at Washington. I later arranged with the U. S. Geological Survey for the printing of a large number of copies of the Oklahoma map, 8,000 copies in all, 5,000 of which were to be sold at Washington, and 3,000 to be taken over by the Oklahoma Survey to be distributed in the state.

In anticipation of the publication of this map, I began to prepare a bulletin which I called *Index to the Stratigraphy of Oklahoma*. In this bulletin was described as nearly as possible every geological formation outcropping in the state, giving the nomenclator (the man who first named it), with date, the character, thickness, areal extent, correlation, and a list of characteristic fossils—the latter data being prepared by Professor Decker. This report was published in September, 1925, as Bulletin 35 and was well received by geologists. As one Texan expressed it: "Red River has always been to me a Chinese wall as far as geology is concerned, but your 'Index' has helped me to scale this wall."

Among other manuscripts was a thick one on *Coal in Oklahoma*. In 1908 I had assigned Bulletin Number 4 to the coal report, and now in 1924, sixteen years later, it was still unpublished and remained a blank in the series. One of the principal reasons for bringing Mr. Shannon from Indiana to the Oklahoma Survey in 1910 was that he might complete the coal report. When I resigned, in talking over policies with Ohern, I suggested that there were two particularly important things to be done, the coal report and the colored geological map. When Ohern resigned in 1914 and turned the administration over to Shannon, he passed on to him these two important items. Shannon had done much work on the report, but the lack of printing funds had prevented its publication. So we all set to work to get out the coal report.

The next legislature gave us a fair appropriation, and we were able to take on another man. Redfield and I, with the help of some part-time student assistants, had been doing practically all the work. I secured as chief geologist Chalmer L. Cooper. In 1927, J. O. Beach joined the staff and soon proved to be one of the most efficient men in the office. He is still connected with the survey. The first task that I assigned to Cooper was to edit the coal report. Much of the manuscript was out of date and had to be discarded. Cooper spent some time in the field in eastern Oklahoma, bringing the report up to date, had maps drawn, and finally saw the report through the press.

About this time I was in the East and stopped at Columbus, Ohio, to discuss some matters with my old friend J. A. Bownocker, then state geologist of Ohio. While there I happened to be in the survey library, and the librarian asked me, "Dr. Gould, when is Bulletin Number 4 of the Oklahoma Survey to be published?"

"Probably never," I said. "The coal report which was to have been Bulletin Number 4 is about ready for the press, but we have already published Number 35, and we plan to leave Number 4 a blank and call the coal report Bulletin Number 36."

"Oh, that will never do," said the young lady. "Don't you see that if Number 4 is left blank in the series the librarians everywhere will always be writing you about it? Publish something as Number 4, no matter what, and complete the series. It is not good policy to leave a blank in the series."

And so our coal report is Bulletin Number 4, published in July, 1926, sixteen years after it was first started.

One of the early superintendents of the Osage Nation was Laban Miles, a Quaker. During the eighties a nephew of Miles, an orphan boy, named Herbert Hoover, spent some time with his uncle at Pawhuska. In the course of time he entered Leland Stanford University and fell under the influence of John C. Branner, then head of the Department of Geology.

Branner had been state geologist of Arkansas before going to Stanford and had left some unfinished work in that state. One summer he sent young Hoover back to complete the mapping of some formations in the coal fields east of Fort Smith. On his way, Hoover stopped off at Pawhuska to visit his uncle Laban Miles.

An appropriation had been secured to erect a building at the Indian agency at Pawhuska. Stone for the building was plentiful, but there was no lime for mortar. Knowing that his nephew was a geologist, Miles put him on a horse and started him out to locate a ledge of limestone for burning into lime. After a few days in the saddle, Hoover found a ledge of rock suitable for the desired purpose, three miles west of town. At this place Agent Miles established a lime kiln which supplied the lime used in many of the early stone buildings in and around Pawhuska.

James Perrin Smith published an article in the *Journal of Geology* in 1894, in which he named and described the Pawhuska limestone found by Hoover. The name is still in the literature and is recognized throughout the world.

During my second term as state geologist, this same Herbert Hoover became president of the United States. Thinking it would be an appropriate gesture, I suggested erecting a monument to President Hoover composed of the Pawhuska limestone which he had discovered. I did not consider that I was justified in using state funds for this purpose but endeavored to interest citizens of Pawhuska in the matter.

But I did not get anywhere. No one would take the initiative. Later I learned that certain local politicians had instituted a whispering campaign to the effect that Gould was trying to boost a Republican, and so the idea of a monument to the only president who ever named a geological formation in Oklahoma did not materialize.

Another report that was hanging fire was one on *Chemical Analyses of Oklahoma Minerals,* including rocks, oil, gas, water and other raw materials, by A. C. Shead. At the time of the interruption of the work of the Survey, he had taken up teaching in the Department of Chemistry. There was in the vault a manuscript containing several thousand chemical analyses. After considerable delay, this report was published as Bulletin Number 14, thus filling up another gap.

Still later we published as Bulletin Number 12 a reprint of Joseph A. Taff's paper on the *Geology of the Arbuckle and Wichita Mountains,* which had originally appeared as U. S. Geological Survey Professional Paper Number 31. This report, which contained the first descriptions of the granite and the lower Paleozoic rocks of these two mountain ranges, was so popular that it had long been out of print and could rarely be obtained, even in second-hand bookstores. Copies of Taff's paper had sold for as much as twenty-five dollars, and very few of the younger geologists had copies of this important and valuable report. After considerable thought and numerous consultations with leading geologists, we decided to republish this paper. It was reprinted as Taff wrote it, without addition or alterations, and proved popular with the geologists. The publication of these three reports filled the gaps in the series of the survey publications.

Much of the success for the publications of the survey is due to the activities of C. L. Cooper, who for six years served as editor. I turned the entire responsibility of this work over to him. Cooper edited the manuscripts and prepared the printing specifications, which were submitted to the State Board of Affairs. After the contract for printing had been let, he saw the report through the press. He read first galley proof, second galley proof, first page proof, and second page proof. He had charge of the preparation of maps and illustrations, and when the report was finally ready for printing, he usually spent several days with the printer, seeing that everything was arranged

224

exactly according to specifications. One who has had no experience in these matters can have very little idea of the extreme care that must constantly be taken in order to avoid mistakes in the printing of a book.

Mr. Cooper seemed to be especially fitted for this kind of work. Careful, industrious, efficient, with a good knowledge of English and a keen eye for detail, he labored faithfully to turn out good reports. And the thirty reports of printed matter published during the six years he was with the survey bear testimony to his careful and painstaking work.

One of the most interesting paleontological discoveries ever made in Oklahoma was the uncovering of a part of the carapace or bony shell of a prehistoric mammal, *Glyptodon*, in a gravel pit near Frederick, by a party of scientists from the University. The *Glyptodon* was a huge beast something like a giant turtle, covered with a shell, an inch thick, made up of great numbers of bony plates dovetailed together.

The pit from which the fossil was taken is located about a mile north of Frederick and near the south end of a long ridge which ends rather abruptly at this place. This ridge stretches northward toward the Wichita Mountains, twenty-five miles distant, and throughout most of its course it is covered with sand and gravel to a depth of ten to fifteen feet. Geologists believe this ridge represents the bed of a prehistoric river, which probably flowed south, and that this river channel was once lower than the surrounding country.

Some months before our visit, the owner, Mr. Holloman, began finding in his gravel pit a number of bones of various kinds of animals. Associated with the bones, he discovered some implements which appeared to him to show that they were the work of man. Among other things, he found seven metates, or flat grinding stones, such as are used by primitive peoples for grinding grain. He also claimed to have dug out of the pit two flint arrowheads and a bead with a hole pierced through the center. Two scientists from outside the state visited Frederick and secured and carried away the greater part of the bones and artifacts which Mr. Holloman had collected.

Articles describing the finds at Frederick appeared in several scientific magazines. Later the deposits were visited by Oliver P. Hay, the veteran paleontologist of the U. S. National Museum. According to Hay, the animal bones which were found in the loose gravel beds and in connection with a flint arrowhead were identified as the bones of three species of primitive elephants, two species of camel, two species of ground sloths, a *Glyptodon*, and at least three species of fossil horses.

The party from the University consisted of C. E. Decker, Leslie Spier of the department of anthropology, Lois Gould, and myself. One of the most important discoveries was the finding of a considerable portion of the carapace or shell of the *Glyptodon*. At the time of the discovery, Mr. Holloman and I happened to be walking together in the gravel pit when we noticed in the loose gravel and sand at our feet some fragments of bone. On kicking around in the loose sand we picked up several bony plates, each about the size of the top of a teacup, with rosette-like markings.

We called the rest of the party and all of us began picking up specimens and digging in the gravel. A foot beneath the surface we found a pavement of bone, a solid mass of plates, still intact, which we soon recognized as the carapace of a *Glyptodon*. After the sand had been removed we found that the portion of the carapace which had been preserved was about five feet in length and three feet wide, containing about 350 plates. Some one hundred more plates were found scattered loosely in the soil and gravel. Only a small part of the bony skeleton remained. The portion which we removed is shaped something like a shallow dish. The greater number of the plates

226

had been carried away by plow and scraper, and are now probably serving for road material somewhere on the highways of Tillman County.

If, as we now believe, the artifacts shaped by human hands were found in the Frederick gravel pit along with the bones of *Glyptodon*, elephant, camel, primitive horse, and ground sloth, it sets the advent of the first known man in America back a very long way into the remote past.

The largest and perhaps the most important publication was Bulletin Number 40, *Oil and Gas in Oklahoma*. Oil is Oklahoma's most valuable mineral resource. Starting in 1900 with a few thousand barrels valued at $10,000, the amount of money derived from oil increased until it reached $500,000,000 annually. Year by year the relation of geology and such other sciences as paleontology, petrography, and physics to the discovery of oil became more apparent.

In 1916–17, Mr. Shannon and L. E. Trout published Bulletin Number 19, entitled *Petroleum and Natural Gas in Oklahoma*. This bulletin was very popular and was soon exhausted, and copies, when obtainable, sold as high as fifty dollars each. There was an insistent demand, not only from geologists, but especially from businessmen and the general public for the publication of a new bulletin on oil and gas. We were not only willing but anxious to prepare and publish such a bulletin, but lacked the funds. Our appropriation for printing was ample and we could pay draftsmen to prepare the maps, but we had no money for going into the field to secure the data. Neither were there funds to pay for the preparation of manuscripts.

I discussed the matter with a number of geologists, and presented our problem before several geological societies, explaining our predicament, and we were delighted by their generous response. Various men volunteered their services in preparing reports. They worked entirely without compensation for the good of the cause. While the members of the survey staff helped wherever possible, still, without the active, sympathetic help of these men who prepared and donated the manuscripts, the bulletin could never have been published. A debt of gratitude is due not only from myself, but also from the general public to these loyal geologists for their unselfish devotion to the cause of science.

This report was issued first as fifty separates, numbered consecutively from A to XX. The various separates were then assembled into three cloth-bound volumes aggregating 1,445 pages. There were more than 100 maps and cross sections. Two of the most popular of the separates were 40 Q, *Digest of Oklahoma Oil and Gas Fields,* compiled by Bess Mills-Bullard, and 40 R, *Petroleum Geology in Oklahoma,* by Sidney Powers.

Dr. Hans Dannenburg, one of the outstanding European geologists, an authority on coal deposits throughout the world, was visiting America studying the various coal fields. In the course of time he came to Oklahoma and found his way to the office of the Geological Survey. Oklahomans are always pleased to show visitors over the Arbuckle Mountains, and so we arranged for a carload of geologists to accompany Dannenburg to the mountains.

We drove south from Norman to Lexington and started to cross the Canadian River bridge. It was a hot, windy summer day, so common in Oklahoma. As we drove up on the bridge the sand was blowing. Dr. Dannenburg looked first upstream, then downstream at the flat, yellow, sandy bed with no water showing and clouds of fine sand filling the air.

"Mine Gott!" said the doctor, "Vot vas dot?"

"That's a river," said I.

"Ein river, vot kind ein river?"

"Oh, just one of our Oklahoma streams."

"Ein Oklahoma river! Vot vas its name?" he inquired.

228

I told him it was the Canadian River.

"Canadian River! Und how long vas it?"

I thought a moment and answered, "About seven hundred miles long."

"Und how vide?"

"About a mile."

"Und how deep?"

"Well, just now on a day like this there is no water at all on the surface. All the water sinks into the sand."

Dannenburg thought the thing over. He looked upstream, then looked downstream at the whirling mass of sand obscuring the bed of the river. At last he muttered to himself. "Mine Gott! Vot ein river! Seven hundred miles long, ein mile vide, and no deep at all."

Again Oklahoma elected as governor a man who appeared to be totally uninformed regarding the real work of a Geological Survey, and in April, 1931, he vetoed the Survey appropriations which had been passed by the legislature. Strangely enough, this governor was not impeached but served out his full term, and so the second hiatus in survey activities lasted for four years. During this period Professor Decker again acted as custodian.

In July, 1935, Mr. Robert H. Dott became director of the Oklahoma Geological Survey. His chief assistant was J. O. Beach.

CHAPTER 10

FIVE YEARS WITH THE
NATIONAL PARK SERVICE

ON SEPTEMBER 29, 1935, Nina passed away. For several years she had had charge of the women's work in Oklahoma for the Federal Emergency Relief Administration, directing the work of some fifteen hundred women, and had been working beyond her strength. In July of that year, she submitted to a surgical operation from which she never recovered.

In undertaking the work as a geologist for the National Park Service, I was motivated by several considerations, the most important of which was the opportunity afforded me to enlarge my knowledge of southwestern geology. I was already well acquainted with the geology of the states of the Great Plains and the lower Mississippi Valley. But I knew little, at first hand, of western Colorado or western New Mexico, and nothing about Arizona, Utah, or Nevada. This appeared to me to be a good chance to explore an interesting region and, insofar as I might, to complete my third self-imposed task, to know the geology of the Southwest. My work was in the states of Arkansas, Oklahoma, Kansas, Texas, New Mexico, Utah, Colorado, Arizona and Nevada.

In this region there were seven national parks and twenty-six national monuments. In addition there were a number of state and municipal parks which were being developed by the

Civilian Conservation Corps (C.C.C.) under the direction of the Park Service.

I joined the Park Service December 1, 1935, and remained until February 1, 1940, during which time I prepared 251 geological reports. During the first two years, the headquarters of the region was at Oklahoma City, then it was moved to Santa Fé, New Mexico. The members of the headquarters staff usually numbered between fifty and seventy-five people, including the administrative, fiscal, technical, and clerical divisions. The technical branches included design, engineering, history, forestry, wild life, archaeology, and geology.

About two-thirds of my time was spent in the field and one-third in the office. It has always been my practice to write up the first draft of my field notes while they are fresh in my mind. In the covered-wagon days on the plains, many was the time when I sat in my tent by the light of a smoking lantern while the rest of the men were sleeping, and mosquitoes buzzed and whined about my ears, writing first impressions of the day's work. And so in the Park Service; after visiting an area I always tried to see to it that, before retiring, my notes were written in longhand. The rough draft of the notes would be mailed to the regional office, and typescript would be awaiting me on my return from the field. It was then an easy matter to correct the notes, add pertinent data, and submit a finished report.

Travel in the eight states was usually by automobile. Sometimes on urgent trips for long distances, I would take a train or airplane. On the automobile trips I was sometimes accompanied by another technician, perhaps an engineer, a wild-life man, or a forester, but on many of the longer itineraries, I traveled alone.

On returning from a field trip, I would find my basket full to overflowing with all sorts of matters requiring attention; letters to be answered, projects to be checked, reports to be examined, and much accumulated paper work to be gone over, but I spent

231

as little time as possible in the office and as soon as the basket was emptied I was off again.

A considerable part of my work concerned the attempt to secure water for the various parks and monuments. In the eastern part of the region, the matter of securing adequate supplies of potable water is not a difficult task, but the farther west one goes, the greater becomes the problem. Arkansas, eastern Oklahoma, and eastern Texas all lie within the humid belt, where the annual rainfall averages forty to fifty inches. Western Texas, western Oklahoma, and parts of eastern New Mexico and Colorado are in the semi-arid belt, with rainfall averaging fifteen to thirty inches a year. Farther west is the arid region, with yearly rainfall running from eight to fifteen inches.

It is rarely difficult to locate ample water supplies anywhere in the humid regions. Springs or flowing streams are usually available at most park sites in Arkansas, eastern Texas, and eastern Oklahoma. Or, if springs or streams are not available, wells can frequently be located so as to encounter underground water supplies. But as one goes west, the conditions become increasingly difficult, and in many cases it becomes necessary to build dams in order to store water. Sheet-metal catchment areas are sometimes installed, as at Mesa Verde National Park and Grand Canyon National Monument. Advantage must always be taken of springs, and as a last resort it is frequently necessary to attempt to secure water from wells.

And it is here that the real grief and trouble begin. No one knows as well as a geologist who had been up against the proposition for many years, that a hole in the ground is always a gamble. I have often said that the only sure thing about an oil well is that someone will have good money in a hole in the ground. No one can possibly tell in advance of drilling whether oil or water may be found underground at any particular place.

True, the geologist sometimes can eliminate unlikely locations and thus reduce the risk. By studying the outcrops of rocks, he may be able to locate the water well in a likely spot, but even then his guess may be wrong. In many instances it has been found necessary to pipe water considerable distances.

It is in the desert country that one bumps squarely up against the overwhelming and fundamental fact that "water is life." You doubtless remember reading in Eugene Manlove Rhodes' fascinating book *West Is West,* the story of Sandy McGregor, the outlaw, fresh from the loot of Luna. He had been driven from his mountain fastness by pursuers on horseback, and in order to escape, he had started to cross the desert. He did so only because there had been heavy rains, and he knew there would be water in the *tinajas,* the rock waterholes, otherwise he would not have attempted it. For, as McGregor says, "Hunger and great weariness, pain and jostling death I can make shift to bear, but against the naked thirst can no man strive for long."

Rarely, indeed, is it possible to get across to the average person from the East the basal, elemental fact that in the arid regions, land is nothing, water is everything. Throughout the Southwest, a man without water may starve to death on ten thousand acres of land, but with water he may live and raise a family on ten acres.

Mesa Verde National Park in southwestern Colorado is an example of the difficulties confronting the geologist and engineer in attempting to secure water for recreational areas in the Southwest. Mesa Verde, the "green tableland," is so called because juniper and piñon trees give it a verdant tone. It is fifteen miles long and eight miles wide, bounded on all sides by steep cliffs, in places two thousand feet high. Into this mesa a number of precipitous high-walled canyons have been cut, and in the caves, or overhanging rock shelters, along the walls of these canyons, some of the best-preserved cliff dwellings in America are found. The primitive people who built their homes in these caves a thousand years ago secured water from weak springs under the cliffs or stored water by building small earthen dams across shallow arroyos atop the mesa.

But when a road had been built to the top of the cliff, and thousands of tourists came to see the prehistoric structures, this source of water soon became inadequate, and it was necessary to secure water by some other method. The first attempt was the installation of a sheet-iron catchment, two acres in extent, in order to preserve the rainwater, which was stored in cisterns. When it rained, this plan was a success, but during the summer months when visitors were most plentiful, rain sometimes did not occur for several weeks, and the cisterns had the habit of running dry.

The next attempt to secure water was made by drilling a deep well. Water was encountered at 2,800 feet, but mechanical difficulties have interfered with the production of an adequate supply. The present plan is to attempt to secure water from streams high up in the La Plata Mountains, thirty-five miles distant, and bring this water by gravity through a pipe line to the top of the mesa, then distribute it to the various utility areas.

At White Sands National Monument, New Mexico, there is water in plenty to be found in wells at a depth of five to ten feet, but unfortunately, it is vile, unpalatable, and not usable. The White Sands are composed entirely of minute crystals of gypsum, which is calcium sulphate, and this mineral has impregnated all the water, so that it is not drinkable. The White Sands Monument is a very popular resort and several thousand people sometimes visit the area the same day, so that considerable quantities of water are required. All the water used on the monument had been hauled in truck tanks from Alamogordo, eighteen miles distant.

One of my early assignments with the Park Service was to

attempt to find a source of potable water that would be adequate in amount for this monument. After discussing the matter with several ranchmen, I finally selected a spring located in Dog Canyon in the Sacramento Mountains. It was necessary to purchase the property containing this spring, and to build a pipe line approximately fifteen miles long in order to carry this water to the monument.

The Natural Bridges National Monument, Utah, was set aside in 1908, but no provision has ever been made for securing water. The custodian either hauls water from Mustang Spring, twelve miles distant, in five-gallon milk cans or carries water nearly a quarter of a mile up a steep trail from a rock waterhole in the bottom of a canyon.

Organ Pipe Cactus National Monument in southwestern Arizona, containing 330,000 acres, is located in the driest, hottest, and most inaccessible part of the Arizona desert. In this entire area there are only two wells, both used by stockmen. Several unsuccessful attempts were made to secure water by drilling at the place where it was planned to locate the headquarters buildings. Finally, water was secured in a well several miles distant, and the headquarters of the monument are to be located near this well.

At Carlsbad Cavern, water for the human-use area is piped six miles from Rattlesnake Springs and raised more than 800 feet. More than 25,000 gallons a day have been used at this place.

For several years, water from the San Francisco Mountains was hauled by train a distance of more than fifty miles to supply the South Rim at Grand Canyon. Later, a pump was installed to raise the water 2,000 feet from a spring at Indian Gardens. On the North Rim, the water is raised 3,800 feet through a four-inch pipe line from a spring located alongside Bright Angel Creek. Part of the flow from the spring passes through turbines that generate power for electric pumps to furnish the "juice" for the lift. The machinery was lowered from the Canyon Rim on a four-mile tramway built for that purpose.

In addition to the parks and monuments listed above, the following areas, at some time, have had difficulty in securing domestic water for the headquarters area: Capulin, Black Canyon of the Gunnison, Arches, Navajo, Canyon de Chelly, El Morro, Gran Quivira, Wupatki, Sunset Crater, Saguaro, and Petrified Forest. Some of the monuments that have an adequate supply of water from springs, streams, or wells, are: Pipe Spring, Aztec Ruin, Yucca House, Montezuma Castle, Tonto, Tumacacori, Chiricahua, Casa Grande, and Bandelier.

Some very interesting experiences came my way during the examinations of new areas that were being considered either for national parks or for monuments, or even for state parks. Throughout the Southwest there are so many areas of unusual interest, from the standpoint of scenery, geology, botany, history, or archaeology, that it is often not so much a question of what to include as it is of what to exclude. Many areas which, if found in an Eastern state, would almost certainly be set aside for public use, here are passed over with little or no consideration.

Omitting the areas which I examined and recommended for state parks, let me discuss briefly some of the places that were being considered for national parks and monuments. All the areas examined for national parks were in national forests. For some years it has been the policy of the Forest Service to set aside "primitive areas," the idea being to preserve these places insofar as possible in their natural state. In the primitive areas no roads are built, except a few truck trails to be used in fire fighting, no lumbering is permitted, and no summer cabins are erected. Many of these primitive areas possessed features which would qualify them for national park status.

One of the primitive areas was in the San Juan and Rio

Grande National forests in the San Juan Mountains in south-western Colorado, and another in the Gila National Forest in southwestern New Mexico.

The San Juan Mountains are an isolated group of high mountains. It is a region of great scenic beauty with many mountain peaks rising to over 13,000 feet in height, and some to more than 14,000 feet. There are numerous flowing streams, with water falls, and many small lakes; the country is heavily timbered throughout with pine, spruce, fir, and aspen.

Starting at Durango, Colorado, our party of five technicians first worked east around the south side of the region. There being no roads into the primitive area, it was necessary to follow the general plan of a mouse nibbling on a piece of cheese and work around the edges. The method pursued was to drive by auto as far as possible up one of the creeks, then proceed either on foot or on horseback as far as might be in one day's travel, returning each night to Durango or some other town. In this manner we investigated six streams on the south side of the Continental Divide, then proceeded to the Rio Grande Forest north of the Divide and inspected the area near the Rio Grande Reservoir.

In the matter of geology, the San Juan Primitive Area has everything. I know of no region of equal size in North America that has so complete, and yet so complicated, a geological history as has the one which we visited. So outstanding is the geology of the San Juan Mountains that for many years several of the larger universities of the United States have had summer schools of geology here, and many of the most noted geologists of this country and of Europe have studied the rocks exposed in these mountains.

Here are the highlights, the major steps in the geological history of the San Juan Mountains. There have been seven great series of geological events, seven acts in the geologic drama.

237

First: The occurrence of the Pre-Cambrian rocks, including granites, schists and gneisses, which have been intruded by greenstone with hornblende-gneiss. After this came elevation and erosion, accompanied by deposits of conglomerate, then more intrusions of granite, followed by mountain building, then uplift, and still later by peneplanation, at which time the mountains were worn down, presumably to a comparatively level plain. This chain of events probably occupied hundreds of millions of years, perhaps longer than all subsequent geologic time.

Second: The region was submerged by marine waters in which rocks of practically all the geological ages were laid down. These rocks are chiefly sandstones, limestones, and shales, arranged in strata or layers, one above the other and aggregating many thousand feet in thickness. For the greater part of this long period of deposition, the region remained under water, but there were several temporary emergences.

Third: At the close of Cretaceous time, the rocks over the entire area were raised as an immense dome, many thousands of feet above their original position. This was about the time of the Laramide revolution, when the greater part of western North America, including the Rocky Mountains, was uplifted.

Fourth: Then came another period of erosion. The top of the dome was worn away by nature's tools, until practically all of the stratified rocks had been removed from the center of the uplift. Today these formations may be seen dipping away from the central mass in all directions, around the periphery of the San Juan Mountains.

Fifth: During Tertiary times, there occurred a great series of volcanic eruptions accompanied by extrusions of lava. Studies by geologists have shown at least six periods of vulcanism, each producing various kinds of volcanic rock. These materials were piled up, one series above another, and in places covered the area to a depth of several thousand feet, occupying hundreds of square miles. Many of the high peaks in the San Juan Mountains consist of remnants of these volcanic rocks.

Sixth: The next act in the drama was glaciation. In the mountains, there are traces of four periods of glacial activity. During these times ice covered the area and, on melting, left behind deposits of various kinds, rock-debris in the form of moraines. In many places, the bedrock has been grooved and striated by glacial action. The two hundred small lakes in the San Juan Mountains occur chiefly where glacial moraines have dammed the narrow valleys, or where ice gouged out rock basins.

Seventh: And finally, the last act of the drama, recent erosion, mountain sculpturing, and the carving of valleys by stream action which have given the mountains their present form and shape. For the most part, the high peaks and ridges are composed of the harder and more resistant rocks, chiefly granite and hard volcanics, which have remained behind when the softer rocks had been carried away.

In the inspection of the Primitive Area in the Gila National Forest, a somewhat different technique was employed. We drove our car from Silver City, north as far as there were any roads, and then took saddle horses for the rest of the inspection, making headquarters at a ranch house near Gila Hot Springs, and at ranger stations.

From the standpoint of geology, this country is very different from the San Juan Mountains, being a relatively flat tableland, composed almost entirely of lava flows. Into this plateau, canyons have been cut by the action of streams which form the headwaters of Gila River. These canyons vary from twenty to forty miles in length, averaging one-fourth of a mile wide, and the canyon walls, five hundred to a thousand feet in height, are in most places perpendicular. The flat uplands are covered with forests.

The region has much of archaeological interest. There are

239

hundreds of prehistoric ruins, both pueblo-community houses, located chiefly in the canyons, and cliff dwellings. The pottery found here is of a distinct type not found elsewhere, and is known as Upper Gila pottery.

One assignment given me which I enjoyed very much was the preparation of a report on the Jemez Mountain Area, with reference to having it set aside as a national park. The Jemez Mountains located west of the Rio Grande, some forty miles northwest of Santa Fé, are roughly circular in outline, with a diameter of thirty to forty miles. The greater part of the rocks in the mountains are of volcanic origin. The outstanding feature is the immense extinct crater on the summit. This crater averages thirteen miles in diameter and the circumference around the rim is approximately fifty miles. It is generally recognized as being the largest known extinct volcanic crater in the world.

Geologists who have studied this crater and the surrounding mountains distinguish at least three periods of volcanic activity, during each of which vast quantities of ashes, cinders, and molten lava were ejected. A considerable amount of this material, being rather fine ash, was caught by prevailing westerly winds and deposited along the east side of the crater, forming the Pajarita Plateau. This ashy material has been compacted by pressure, forming a cream-colored rock known as tuff. The beds of tuff are often separated by layers of hard, black basaltic rock which was formed by the cooling of seething molten lava as it flowed from the crater and spread over the surface. Small streams which take their rise along the slope of the crater have cut deep and narrow canyons into the soft tuff which makes up the greater part of Pajarita Plateau. More than forty of these canyons flow east from Jemez Mountains into the Rio Grande or its tributaries.

This soft tuff being easily worked, formed ideal material in which the Old People could excavate their homes. Some of the finest examples of cliff dwelling to be found in the Southwest occur along the sides of the canyons and on the cliffs in the Pajarita Plateau. Of these the two most famous are at Frijoles Canyon in Bandelier National Monument, and at Puye ruins southwest of Española. On the mesas between the canyons and in some of the canyons themselves, one finds several community houses and hundreds of ruins of small stone dwellings, with the attendant sherds and artifacts. On one of the mesas south of Frijoles Canyon are the noted Stone Lions, two crouching figures about eight feet long, supposed to have been hunting fetishes, carved by prehistoric craftsmen from the soft tuff.

The largest deposit of travertine I have ever seen is at Tonto National Monument, in the deep and narrow valley of Pine Creek, in the noted Tonto Basin, Arizona. Alongside the creek valley are several strong springs issuing from a limestone formation, the water being heavily charged with calcium carbonate. On reaching the surface and being exposed to the air, this water deposits part of its load of calcium carbonate in the form of travertine. Throughout the centuries this travertine has accumulated, forming a natural dam across Pine Creek, until in the course of time a platform was built up, 200 feet high and nearly a quarter of a mile long, completely filling the valley. The water has found its way through crevices in the rock, and has eroded a tunnel beneath the platform, through which the stream now flows.

Texas has no national monument. At different times there has been agitation looking toward establishing a monument in Palo Duro Canyon some twenty to fifty miles southwest of Amarillo. Palo Duro Canyon, which is the longest and deepest gash cut by Nature anywhere on the Great Plains, averages six hundred feet deep and a mile wide. The length is about forty miles.

Several years ago, a state park was established in Palo Duro Canyon; a road was built down the canyon wall and several stone buildings were erected, some on the rim and others in the bottom of the canyon. The proposed plan was to include in the Palo Duro National Monument all the Texas State Park and considerable additional acreage. The general idea was to provide a wildlife refuge for deer, antelope, buffalo, and other animals indigenous to the Great Plains that have either become extinct or are now very rare in this part of North America. On instructions from Washington, I revisited the area and traced the boundaries of the proposed national monument.

For several years, the establishment of a national park in the Arbuckle Mountains of southern Oklahoma had been discussed. I was a member of an inspection party that spent several days traveling over the mountains. We visited the most spectacular areas, including the various waterfalls and other objects of unusual interest, discussed freely the entire situation in the field, and submitted to Washington reports covering the subject.

The decision was to the effect that it was not deemed feasible to establish a national park covering the entire area of the Arbuckle Mountains. Of the several objections raised, the three that carried most weight were: first, the area cannot be considered as possessing unique and outstanding scenic beauty and interest; second, it is much cut up by railroads, highways and industrial plants; and third, there is already a national park (Platt) near the Arbuckle Mountains.

However, it was suggested that it might prove practicable to establish a national monument somewhere in the Arbuckle Mountains, and I was instructed to determine the most favorable location for such a monument. The desirable features of the proposed monument included a good geological section, where the various formations exposed in the mountains could be seen; water, including springs, and, if possible, a good waterfall; timber, shade, and accessibility. From many possible loca-

El Morro from the east.

"Paso por aqui," 1526, Inscription Rock.

Almost seventy and going strong, Big Bend, 1937.

tions it was not easy to make a selection, but I finally chose two outstanding areas, one on the north side of the mountains, the other on the south side, which to my mind embodied the points desired. My report is on file in Washington.

For many years, geologists have known that there were numerous caves large and small in the Guadalupe Mountains in southern New Mexico. The only one of these caves which has been developed is Carlsbad Cavern. The rocks in the entire area, extending for approximately fifty miles west, northwest, and southwest of the cavern, consist of heavy gray limestone, from 2,000 to 3,000 feet thick.

This limestone contains many crevices, fissures, openings, and solution channels, large and small, but many of these openings never reach the surface. The entire mountain is honeycombed with these channels, which have been formed by the action of water on the soluble limestone of the mountain mass. This being true, it is to be expected that from time to time various openings on the surface will be discovered. It is altogether possible that, when the Guadalupe area has been thoroughly explored and developed, parties may go underground in the present Carlsbad Caverns and come to the surface at some other opening five or ten miles distant.

Ice caves occur in several places in the Southwest, but the greatest number are found in western New Mexico between El Morro and Quemado. At this place, an area of approximately one thousand square miles is covered with basaltic lava, and more than thirty different craters, or vents, from which the lava escaped, have been counted.

The ice caves occur in channels or openings in this lava. The only one of these caves that has been exploited, and is now open to visitors, is located near the road from Grants to El Morro. At this place one descends about fifty feet into a channel in the basalt, and near the north end of the opening is a cave, or recess, in which is a solid wall of ice, forty feet long and fifteen feet high, which remains throughout the year.

Mummy Cave, in Canyon del Muerto (Canyon of the Dead) on Canyon de Chelly National Monument, Arizona, contains more than one hundred skeletons which have lain there undisturbed since 1804. In that year, a band of Navajo warriors had gone on a raid, leaving the old men, women, and children, as they thought, safely sheltered in a large cave high up on the canyon wall. A band of Mexicans on a raid into the Navajo country discovered the cave, laid siege to it, and finally massacred all the Navajos. When the Navajo men returned they found that all their relatives had been killed. Being superstitious, the Navajos have avoided the cave ever since, and only a few white people have ever seen it.

The Navajo Indians who live in Canyon de Chelly have a unique and weird system of communication. De Chelly is a twisty canyon thirty miles long, averaging less than a quarter of a mile wide. It is enclosed within precipitous overhanging cliffs three hundred to one thousand feet high. Several hundred Navajo Indians live in conical huts, called hogans, in the bottom of the canyon, where they raise corn, squashes, and peaches. The signals consist of a series of long-drawn-out cries, which to the white man sound like the sound of a wolf. In this way Indians several miles apart can make themselves understood. The cry echoes and reverberates from one cliff to another, literally passing around corners and finally dying out in the distance. When a Navajo wishes to convey a message to his friends, up or down the canyon, he lets out a series of howls which can be interpreted and understood by other Navajos.

Organ Pipe National Monument, recently created in southwestern Arizona, was set aside for the purpose of preserving two rare species, one a plant, the other an animal, found nowhere else in the United States. The organ pipe cactus, for which the monument was named, is related to the giant saguaro cactus, but has multiple stems coming from the root. The Sonoran bighorn sheep, which differs from the bighorn of the Rocky Mountains, is practically extinct, but is found occasionally in the mountains of northern Sonora and southwestern Arizona.

The number of prehistoric dwellings in the four arid states of the Southwest is unknown, but may run well into the hundreds of thousands. Throughout a considerable part of the area, every mesa has its stone buildings, usually spoken of as pueblos, and every canyon has its cliff dwellings. Some of these dwellings on the mesas are one- or two-room masonry structures, while others are community houses containing many rooms, such as those atop the rock at El Morro or Puye. Similarly, some of the cliff dwellings have but a single small room, while others are community houses containing scores of rooms; for instance, those at Mesa Verde National Park or Navajo National Monument. Many of the national parks and monuments in the four states contain prehistoric dwellings, but only a comparatively few of these pueblo ruins have ever been explored.

Two of the finest examples of extinct volcanoes in the Southwest, each with a perfect crater on the summit, are now national monuments. Capulin, in northeastern New Mexico, has a winding road leading to the summit which is used by 20,000 tourists a year. But Sunset Crater, one of several cinder cones in the volcanic region known as the San Francisco Mountains, between Flagstaff and Grand Canyon, has no such convenience. The surface of this volcano is covered with fine, loose volcanic ash and cinders, making the climb extremely difficult, so that only a few of the most hardy climbers have ever succeeded in reaching the summit.

At the time of the volcanic eruption which built up this

crater, the country was already inhabited. Remains of the homes of Basket-maker people have been found buried in the black ashes and cinders ejected at the time of the formation of the cinder cone. Beams of some of these ancient dwellings have been recovered, and by the tree-ring method, it has been determined that the eruption which buried the houses occurred between 850 and 900 A.D.

The three most inaccessible national monuments in the Southwest are Wheeler, Rainbow Bridge, and Gila Cliff Dwellings, none of which has custodians. The trail to Wheeler National Monument which is located at timber line in the San Juan Mountains, near Creede, Colorado, is closed by snowdrifts from September to June. Rainbow Bridge is reached by a two-day pack-train trip from Navajo Lodge at the end of the auto road. Gila Cliff Dwellings entails a ten-mile horseback trip.

CHAPTER 11

MORE NATIONAL PARK SERVICE

In the Southwest the Great Architect has used massive tools, has painted with bold strokes, and has produced Gargantuan effects. It is in the Southwest that one may observe the largest and most spectacular geological phenomena to be found anywhere on this continent. Here are the greatest canyon, the largest cavern, the most extensive petrified forest, the largest and highest sand dunes, the longest and highest cliffs, the largest and deepest meteor crater, the largest extinct volcanic crater, the most spectacular erosion forms, and the most complete geological section to be found in North America.

A National Park Service description of the Southwest sets forth the charm of this unique region.

"This Southwest is a land of color, of amazing distances, of the romance of vanished civilizations, and of living cultures closely related to prehistory and vastly differing from the habits and mode of life of the Anglo-Saxon and of the white man generally. Young in years, young in settlement by English speaking peoples, the Southwest has the oldest definite records of human occupancy in the United States; and it was explored and to a certain extent settled by Spanish adventurers and missionaries long before English occupation of the eastern seaboard.

"It was not so many years ago—fifty or sixty—that the tide of population in its westward movement swept into the South-

247

west. Miners, hunters, and trappers, cattlemen—a rough and tough breed—left their history in such towns as Tombstone. Billy the Kid, badman or hero, according to the point of view, was its Robin Hood during his brief span of existence. Geronimo and Cochise, the Apache chieftains, belonged to the region.

"The Southwest is a land of contradictions—of high mountains, tremendous canyons, and flat deserts; of little moisture and yet of torrential downpours that leave broad rivers which for a few days usurp old roadbeds; of abandoned prehistoric ruins hundreds of years old, and of modern motor camps; of lands that lie parched for rain, yet 'bloom like the rose' given a little water; of primitive Indian travel afoot and on horse, yet crossed by transcontinental highways, railways, and airway routes, the latter with high beacons that intrigue the imagination; of enormous, rainbow-hued bridges built by Nature, and of man's great engineering feats in bridge building and in conquering the mighty rivers that were Nature's tools in her bridge and canyon building.

"In all, it is a land of fascination, with its scenery, its traditions, and its relics of the past. Enchanted it has been called; mysterious, gorgeous, multicolored, primitive, romantic, artistic, vibrant—then adjectives fail, and the writer confesses that words cannot convey to the uninitiated the glory that is the Southwest."

I have often been asked this question, "What is the most interesting spot in the Southwest?" The question is not easy to answer; there are so many places of interest. Perhaps no two of us would agree. The things that appeal to you might not appeal to me. Our experience, our training, our viewpoints are so different. My choice is Inscription Rock in El Morro National Monument, sixty miles south of Gallup, New Mexico. May I tell you why?

El Morro is a great rock, a sheer cliff two hundred feet high,

248

shouldering out into a flat plain like the prow of a gigantic battleship. The rock is of gray and buff sandstone—the Navajo sandstone of the geologists. The Navajo and its associated formations are the great cliff-makers of the Southwest. Echo Cliffs along Marble Canyon, north of Cameron, Arizona, are of Navajo sandstone. So are the Vermilion Cliffs west of Navajo Bridge, and the cliffs in Navajo National Monument that contain the three immense caves, Betatakin, Keet Seil, and Inscription House, with their prehistoric pueblos. The cliffs at Kanab, Utah, and at Zion National Park are composed of the same Navajo sandstone.

Atop Inscription Rock is another ledge of sandstone, the Dakota. But between the Navajo and the Dakota is an unconformity, representing a hiatus, or time interval, of perhaps a million years. In other parts of the Southwest, this gap is represented by the Morrison formation containing dinosaur bones. Out on the flat plain in front of the Rock there are great piles of black, volcanic lava spewed out by internal fires, and looking across to the slope of the Zuñi Mountains one sees ledges of gray limestone and red shale and sandstone, and even of the primitive granite. So that from the viewpoint of geology, El Morro is outstanding.

And so with vegetation. Three life zones meet here. On the surrounding plain one sees a typical Upper Sonoran flora. Piñon and juniper are the two dominant trees which mark this zone through half a dozen southwestern states. Yucca, cactus, and several small shrubs complete the flora belonging to this life zone. But growing along the Rock there are other trees which mark the lower part of the Transition Zone. *Pinus ponderosa*, or western yellow pine, is the dominant tree. Associated with the pine are two other types characteristic of the lower Transition, namely oak and alligator-bark juniper.

But it is neither the geology nor the botany that makes El

Morro famous. The interest is chiefly archaeological and historical. For here, as nowhere else on the North American continent, one may see seven separate and distinct types of American culture.

Long before the white man set foot on our shores, the prehistoric American lived on and beside the Rock. Atop the Rock there are ruins of two community houses, each with more than one hundred rooms, not yet excavated, the homes of the Old People. On the face of the rock are petroglyphs and paintings in color, the latter representing the sun, moon, and rainbow. The carvings are of men, goats, the winged serpent, birds, hands, feet, and symbols of various kinds. For this was once a thickly settled region. On the various mesas, and out on the plain east of the Rock, there are literally hundreds of pueblo ruins, the sites of once happy homes. These people lived, worked, evolved a pattern of life and a religion, and died here. The records they carved on the Rock help to tell their story. Archaeologists classify them as late-prehistoric Zuñi sites, and tell us that they flourished about six hundred years ago.

Then came another race of people, the *Conquistadores,* to enjoy for brief periods the comfort and security of the Rock. At the foot is a spring, all too rare in this land of little water, with grateful shade in the shadow of the great Rock, and from oak, pine, and juniper which cluster at its base. Here the leaders with their retinues of soldiers, padres, and Indians, paused and refreshed their horses and their men. While resting, they inscribed with their daggers on the Rock their names, the date, and something of their work. The phrase, *Paso por aqui,* "passed by here," used over and over again, introduces many of these inscriptions. Starting with the story of Oñate in 1607, there is an almost continuous record of 160 years of exploration and conquest. The last Spanish inscription is dated 1772.

250

Charles F. Lummis and others have described many of the inscriptions. The record has gripping interest, but the complete story of the strivings, the hopes and fears, conquests and defeats of these *muy elegante caballeros,* "the very gallant gentlemen," is still in the inkpot. But the Rock, grim, foreboding, standing sentinel against the rising sun, took little note of the coming or the passing of these strong, virile leaders who blazed the first highway across a continent. They passed this way, left here their record, but for which many of them would have faded into oblivion.

Less than half a decade after the date of the last inscription, a new nation was born. A nation of vigorous, resourceful people whose two dominant traits were religious liberty and land hunger. Originally only a row of colonies along the Atlantic coast, this young sturdy nation soon began to experience growing pains, and, following its manifest destiny, began to stretch farther west. The Louisiana Purchase, the Florida purchase, the annexation of Texas, and the Mexican War were but incidents in the march of an empire to reach the western ocean.

Then came the Mormons seeking escape from persecution in the eastern states. Not the more famous expedition under Brigham Young, but the less known colony that used the southern route. They, too, carved their names as they rested by the water and shade, and then passed westward.

Again the Rock, patient and serene, had its part in the western trek. Major Simpson, in 1849, rested his United States troops here by the water and the shade. His name and that of R. H. Kern, the artist of the expedition, record the event.

Next came the Argonaut, the gold seeker, pursuing the yellow metal in California. Children and grandchildren of these hardy pioneers who crossed the country in wagon trains drawn by patient oxen now come in high-powered automobiles. Some

251

give the Rock and its inscriptions only a cursory glance and hurry away to the next place, complaining that the roads are not paved.

Then the cattleman, the first since the Indian to make here a permanent abode. The nutritious grasses lured him, and he watered his herds at the spring. The booted and spurred cowboy, resting in the shade of the Rock on hot afternoons, carved thereon cattlebrands and names famous to Cowland.

And lastly, sprawled over all others, the modern tourist has carved his plebeian name.

So, to go back to my original statement: The Rock has outstanding geology, typical plant association, striking archaeology, and abundant history, exemplifying seven distinct types of American culture: the Indians, the Spanish conquistador, the Mormon, the American soldier, the gold seeker, the cowman, and of course, the ubiquitous modern tourist. Where else on this continent is there such another autograph album?

Nowhere on this whirling planet may puny man see a better demonstration of Nature's three fundamental processes, deposition, elevation, and erosion, than at Grand Canyon National Park, Arizona. First, the rocks were deposited as layers, one above another in the bottom of long-gone, prehistoric seas; next these rock layers were elevated by some tremendous force above their original position, and, finally, the rocks were eroded and worn away and their fragments carried to some other place.

These three processes are eternal and fundamental, always in operation, never ceasing, never completed. From the time when the morning stars first sang together, even until time shall be no more, without haste and without rest, these three processes have been constantly at work, making over and reshaping the earth. But so slowly, so quietly has this work been accomplished that we are rarely conscious of it. We each play our own little part in the drama of life, and leave the stage to others, taking small account of the universal drama which goes on all about us.

Grand Canyon is two hundred miles long, a mile deep, and averages ten miles wide. There is nothing else quite like it anywhere. But it didn't just happen, neither has it always been there. The story of the development of Grand Canyon has been written in the rocks so that he who runs may read. All that is needed is the seeing eye and the understanding mind.

When you mount a mule and take the Bright Angel Trail winding back and forth from the Canyon rim at El Tovar, down and ever down to the Colorado River, you will see the rock layers that make up the walls of the canyon. The three most abundant kinds of stratified rocks, shales, sandstones and limestones, are much in evidence, layer after layer, lying level one above another, some hard, some soft, with a total combined thickness of three thousand feet. In these rock layers there are fossils, evidences of extinct life, showing the progressive development from primitive, one-celled forms to large lizard-like animals. Finally, you come to the Inner Gorge, and still the trail leads downward across another kind of rock. These are all very hard rocks, granites and gneisses and schists, not arranged in level beds or layers, but rumpled, twisted and contorted into fantastic shapes. And so, at last, to the bridge over the Colorado River, here a muddy, turbulent stream, flowing swiftly between precipitous cliffs, rushing madly on its way to the Western Ocean.

Four of the five major divisions of geological time are represented along the canyon wall. Within the Inner Gorge we find granites and other associated rocks belonging to the Archaeozoic and Proterozoic eras. This is the original earth stuff, the "basal complex," the material from which all other rocks have been formed, that goes downward toward the center of the earth. The level lying beds that make up the upper three thousand feet of the Canyon wall belong chiefly to the Paleozoic era, including Cambrian, Devonian, Mississippian, and Permian beds. And at one place one finds red sandstones and shales, part of the Moenkopi formation, the lowest member of the Triassic, of the Mesozoic era.

Now these things which I have attempted to describe so briefly are very obvious. We can see the rocks, we can feel them, and if the Ranger isn't watching, we can even pick up a fragment and carry it home so that we may impress the neighbors by saying nonchalantly, "I found this in Grand Canyon." But constantly our minds are inquiring, how, why, when, what caused all this? And, to the best of my ability I shall try to answer some of the questions.

The history of Grand Canyon is long—very long. The granite now being exposed in the bottom of the Inner Gorge is among the oldest rock exposed anywhere on the surface of the earth.

How many years? Oh, say eight hundred to one thousand million years. In fact, nobody knows, but this is as good a guess as any.

Then, throughout unnumbered ages the geologic column was slowly built up. Shales, sandstones, limestones, layer upon layer, were washed in from long-vanished surrounding land masses and laid down on the bottom of a long-departed ocean, or along vanished shore lines. There are eleven different formations or layers exposed in the canyon walls. Some geologists believe that one of these formations, the Coconino sandstone, may have been deposited chiefly as deserts and dunes.

Eventually the layer cake was done. The rock layers had all been deposited, one above another. Then the seas drained away, and the country stood as dry land. Rivers began flowing across the surface of the land. Water falling as rain in distant mountains formed small rivulets, which came together forming larger and still larger streams, and these finally united into a great river, the second in size in the United States, which today we call the Colorado.

This stream, taking its rise along the backbone of North America, started on its way to the Pacific. It flowed in a general southwesterly course, dodging hills, keeping to the lowest channel, cutting its way through soft rocks, avoiding the harder ledges, often twisting about like a tortured snake, and acting as a normal, well-behaved river is supposed to act. The general course of the Colorado all the way from Long's Peak to the Gulf of California was established in the "dim, dead days beyond recall."

Then something happened. Something is always happening to interrupt the placid, uneventful life of a river, a nation, or an individual. Near the middle course of the Colorado the land surface began acting up. It wouldn't stay put. Some great internal force began elevating the land, something like a giant blister, right across the well-established course of the Colorado River. Imagine an inverted saucer one hundred miles in diameter. Geologists call this bulge the Kaibab Dome or the Kaibab Plateau, and sometimes they say the Kaibab Uplift.

What could a well-behaved, hard-working, respectable river do when things went haywire? Two things: It might either peacefully abandon its course without a fight and flow around the Dome, or it might spit on its hands and buckle down to cut its way across. If the elevation of the Dome had been rapid, undoubtedly the river would have been deflected either to the north or south and its lower course today might have been many hundreds of miles away from its old channel.

But, as it happened, the land rose slowly, very, very slowly; just how fast we do not know, but probably only a few inches a century. So that the river in its down-cutting has been able just about to keep pace with the elevation of the land. Or, to say

255

it differently, the water in the channel of the Colorado River in Grand Canyon was probably never a great deal higher above sea level than it is today. As, throughout the ages, the Kaibab Plateau has slowly risen a fraction of an inch at a time, just so slowly has the river succeeded in cutting its way downward.

In this cutting, the water has been aided by the sand, pebbles, and boulders which are carried in times of flood. These tools of erosion gouge and grind and gnaw and rub and abrade the solid rocks along the banks, and slowly but surely wear them away, constantly widening and deepening the channel.

But the Colorado is not a patient, quiet, kindly stream, as, for instance, the Mississippi or the Ohio, flowing in gentle meanders through flat valleys. Its disposition has been ruined, and it is today a very impatient river, a typical wild-western stream. On its way through the Canyon, it growls and roars and froths. It tumbles over rapids, throwing spray into the air, and slaps at its banks. In every way possible, the Colorado seems to protest at being imprisoned between high walls. But the unheeding walls stand sheer, and its turbulent course continues until, finally, in man-made Lake Mead, one hundred miles above Boulder Dam, the troubled waters come to rest.

And so we may see at Grand Canyon a clear-cut demonstration of Mother Nature's three eternal processes: deposition, elevation, and erosion. It is textbook geology, simple and easy to understand. From the canyon rim, or along the trail, or looking up from the bottom, the rock layers leap to the eye. The most unobservant persons cannot fail to see them. There is nothing else to see.

The outstanding fact about Grand Canyon is that the elevation of the dome and the down-cutting of the stream have been contemporaneous. In most places the rocks have first been elevated, and then the processes of erosion have begun. Nature's tools, rain, running water, wind, frost, heat, chemical agencies, working together, break down the rocks and carry them away. In this manner most land forms have been produced. Hills, valleys, cliffs, canyons, mesas, buttes, and the hundreds of different erosion forms have been shaped chiefly by the action of the agents of erosion on land already elevated. This is the ordinary procedure, as for instance, in the Black Hills, the Ozarks, or the Arbuckle Mountains.

But in the case of Grand Canyon, the two processes are going on at the same time. All available evidence points to the fact that the Kaibab Plateau is still rising—very slowly, it is true, but rising just the same. And we know of a certainty that the Colorado is still sawing its way athwart the slowly rising dome.

Great men of American science have worked in Grand Canyon. In 1872 a party under the direction of one-armed Major John Wesley Powell made the first boat trip down the Canyon and proposed many of the striking names which have since become classic, such as Dirty Devil, Bright Angel, and God's Pocket. Powell was afterward director of the Bureau of American Ethnology and in the latter capacity he did much to establish the foundations of Southwestern archaeology. There is a monument to Powell on the South Rim.

More than sixty years ago, Captain C. E. Dutton, one of Powell's associates, published the first monograph on Grand Canyon. The versatile W. H. Holmes, geologist, ethnologist, and artist, contemporary of Powell and Dutton, who succeeded Powell as director of the Bureau of American Ethnology, made the noted pen sketches of Grand Canyon. Many people believe that his artistic work along this line has never been excelled.

David White, whose ashes repose in the cemetery on the South Rim, was one of the great paleontologists of America. It was White who first found fossil footprints of four-footed amphibia and reptiles embedded in the shale in the canyon walls.

Of all the areas in the Southwest administered by the Park

Service, the Big Bend National Park in Trans-Pecos, Texas was in many respects my favorite, probably because I was on the ground at the time the park was being developed and saw it in its raw state. Big Bend is a semi-arid plain, verging on desert, through which have been thrust a number of volcanic peaks. The area of approximately 750,000 acres is dominated by the Chisos, or Ghost, Mountains, which rise 6,000 feet above the level of the Rio Grande, the stream which forms the southern boundary of the Park and separates it from the Republic of Mexico.

Geologically, the greater part of the Big Bend country is a graben, or down-dropped block, of the earth's crust, forty miles across, where the rocks have been dropped four thousand feet from their original position. Along the south side of the Park, the Rio Grande has cut three deep and narrow canyons, Santa Elena, Mariscal, and Boquillas, athwart uplifted mountain ranges. I have stood on the Texas side of the river at the mouth of Santa Elena Canyon, tossed a pebble across the river into Mexico, and looked straight up the Canyon wall, 1,500 feet.

The rocks abound in fossils. There are myriads of petrified oyster and clam shells, some of them three and four feet in diameter. Bones of dinosaurs and other prehistoric monsters occur, and scattered over the surface one finds petrified wood, one log being ten feet in diameter.

The Chisos Mountains form what the biologists call a biotic unit. Being surrounded on all sides by desert, these mountains contain certain species of plants not usually found in this part of the country. On the Chisos Mountains are groves of aspen trees growing farther south than any other aspens in the United States. The Arizona cypress and piñon occur here, far from their natural habitat. Also Ponderosa pine and Douglas fir, trees which belong high up in the Rocky Mountains. On the lower

Gould, third from right, on the Big Bend Trip.

Cross section through the Arbuckles.

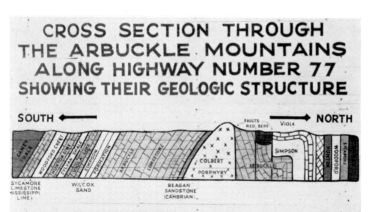

CROSS SECTION THROUGH THE ARBUCKLE MOUNTAINS ALONG HIGHWAY NUMBER 77 SHOWING THEIR GEOLOGIC STRUCTURE

SOUTH ← FAULTS RED BEDS VIOLA → NORTH

THESE BEDDED ROCKS, ORIGINALLY LAID DOWN AS NEARLY HORIZONTAL LAYERS OF MUD AND SAND UNDER THE SEA, FOLDED INTO A HIGH MOUNTAIN RANGE, ABOUT THE TIME THE APPALACHIAN MOUNTAINS WERE FORMED, THIS WAS WORN DOWN BY STREAMS AND BURIED BENEATH LATER SEDIMENTS, WHICH HAVE BEEN STRIPPED AWAY BY EROSION, EXPOSING THE ROOTS OF THE OLD MOUNTAINS.
THESE GEOLOGIC SIGNS WERE ERECTED BY THE LIONS CLUB OF ARDMORE AT THE SUGGESTION OF DR. CHAS. N. GOULD, DIRECTOR OF THE OKLAHOMA GEOLOGICAL SURVEY, WITH THE APPROVAL OF THE STATE HIGHWAY COMMISSION AND ARDMORE GEOLOGICAL SOCIETY.

Friend of the earth at retirement.

slopes one finds the weeping juniper, a tree which grows in Mexico and does not occur elsewhere in the United States.

There are pink and green rattlesnakes, a number of rare birds, three species of deer, the peccary, or javelina, and several other small animals. In caves high up on the Chisos Mountains, the archaeologist finds remains of the homes of prehistoric people, and on the flats between the peaks there are numerous traces of workshops where the aborigine shaped his flint implements.

The propagation of a herd of Texas longhorn cattle, once so common in the state but now fast disappearing, was one of the suggested projects for Big Bend Park. The most difficult problem was to find a tract of land *with water*, suitable for maintaining the herd. Accordingly it was decided to send a pack-train party into the Dead Horse Mountains in the eastern part of the park, north of Boquillas Canyon, to investigate the possibilities of this area as the home for such a herd of cattle. It is a rough, broken country, containing more than one hundred square miles, that had never been explored by Park Service people.

I am giving herewith some excerpts from the notes taken on this trip. Being made in the field, these notes record first impressions:

> "Saturday, October 17, 1937, 3 P.M. Backed up against a mesquite tree on the banks of the Rio Grande, below the mouth of Boquillas Canyon.

"Our party consists of four National Park Service technicians: W. B. McDougall, botanist; A. E. Borrell, mammalogist; Ross A. Maxwell and Charles N. Gould, geologists. As helpers we have 'Waddy' Burnham, a ranchman who furnished the horses, Lloyd Wade, a cowman, now foreman at Big Bend Camp, and Juan Gamboa, as guide. There are twelve horses and Juan's '*mulla*.'

"Juan leads out on the trail. His big Mexican hat is our guiding star. Then comes Borrell, with an eye out for deer, birds, and other forms of wild life. Then Old Roan that packs the chuck in two boxes, and Old Gray that packs the two water kegs, two Dutch ovens, and more grub. Next is Lloyd Wade who keeps Old Gray in the trail; he likes to wander. Then three pack horses, each with a roll of bedding wrapped in a tarp. Then Waddy, who hazes the three pack horses, and lastly the three technicians, McDougall, Maxwell and myself. My horse's name is Nugget, a gentle little bay, whose only fault is in being over-ambitious, always wanting to pass the rest of the outfit and lead the procession.

"Thursday night we drove fifty miles from the headquarters camp in the Chisos Mountains to the Mexican hamlet Boquillas at the head of Boquillas Canyon on the Rio Grande. The horses and a truck which carried the chuck and bedding had preceded us. We had supper and breakfast with Juan Sada, the storekeeper. After sleeping on the ground, we got the horses packed and were on the trail at 9:30 yesterday morning. We started north over the abandoned Strawhouse Trail up Ernst Valley. No water, no stock, and no stop for noon. About four o'clock we headed the valley and crossed the divide into the drainage of Telephone Canyon, as it is locally known, because of the fact that during the Villa insurrection the government built a telephone line down the valley.

"The procession then turned downstream toward the Rio Grande, and luckily about sundown, Juan, who leads the party, found two rock waterholes. We all piled off the horses, unpacked, started a fire of sotol and yucca stalks and Waddy started to make some of his famous bread. Making camp bread is easy if you know how. Just open a sack of flour, stand it on end and scoop out a hole in the top. With a big wooden spoon stir in the right amount of lard, salt, baking powder and water. When it has reached the proper consistency, take out a fistful of dough, flatten it out and dump it on the Dutch oven which has been heating over the campfire. Put on the lid and cover the lid with live coals. In a few minutes you will have a pone of bread, than which there is no tastier. This pone with bacon, coffee, and baked beans out of a can made the evening meal fit for a king, because, as the Spartans said, it was seasoned with the best sauce—hunger.

"Maxwell and I shared a bed. I stretched out, rolled over once, and the next thing I knew Waddy had a fire started and coffee water boiling. Then a mocking bird sang, a quail called, and it was daylight. Soon the sun shone on the high peaks to the west. Waddy made six pones of bread and we had breakfast of bacon, bread, coffee, and apple butter, eaten standing up. We packed and started down the canyon to the Rio Grande, arriving at noon. Camp is in a motte of old, gnarled, twisted mesquite, fifty yards from the Rio. Near by is a deserted 'straw house' built of stalks of reeds standing on end. Across the river is Mexico.

"McDougall and Borrell are writing notes. Wade has just put on a pot of beans. Waddy is fixing a saddle. Maxwell has gone upstream to get a picture of the canyon, and I'm writing notes. Hot during the day but cold at night. Before morning Maxwell pulled up a double thickness of tarp over the three blankets. A little later we're going down to the river and take a bath.

"We are half a mile below the mouth of Boquillas Canyon, where it comes out of the mountains. The cliffs back of us rise two thousand feet. The Rio Grande has cut a narrow, winding gorge twelve miles long across Dead Horse Mountain, but when the river leaves the canyon it flows in broad, sweeping curves across the plain on its way to the Mexican Gulf. Tomorrow we expect to start back up Telephone Canyon, ride 'clean to the head,' to quote Waddy, and plan to make dry camp on top of Dead Horse Mountain—*Sierra del Caballo Muerto.*

"Our object in making the trip is to try to find out if there is enough water and grass in the Dead Horse Mountains to support a herd of longhorn cattle. We are finding that there is plenty of grass on the upper slopes but very little water anywhere, not nearly enough for a sizable herd. The problem will be to get water, either from wells (not so feasible), concrete tanks (a possibility), or by pumping several miles from the Rio Grande on the east, or from Tornillo Creek to the west. This plan may be possible but expensive, as it will entail a constant overhead for pumping.

"We are supposed to be the first National Park technicians ever in this area. It's about the worst trail in Texas, most of the way no trail at all. The horses just pick their way from rock to rock. The mountains are of Lower Cretaceous limestone, several thousand feet thick, repeated by six or eight parallel step faults. Plenty of geology, but monotonous. The limestone is cavernous, full of crevices, caves, and solution channels, and doesn't hold water. No springs, no wells, and few *tinajas.*

Sunday Night, October 18

"We watered the horses in the Rio Grande at daylight and stopped for noon at the *tinajas* where we camped Friday night. Waddy, Wade, and Juan watered twelve thirsty horses by dipping water out of a deep rock waterhole and pouring it into the Dutch ovens for them to drink. Meanwhile, I started a fire and had water boiling. Borrell opened beans and tomatoes and we had lunch standing up in the sun.

"Tonight we are making dry camp on top of the limestone ridge, the main ridge of Dead Horse Mountains. A hot afternoon of climbing with no trail. Just imagine the roughest part of the Arbuckle limestone of Oklahoma with two thousand feet of relief. But the horses are wise, and Juan, who knows every deer trail, found the way.

"Supper is over. I'm backed up against a big yucca log writing this note. The horses have been hobbled, night is closing in. Chisos Mountains stand like a grim sentinel in the dusk, with the horn of the new moon seemingly perched on the highest peak.

Monday Morning

"I awoke in the blue bedroom to see the morning made. The sun was not yet over the valley. Peaks to the north are bathed in bright light. Breakfast almost ready, Juan made the bread. The menu included canned peaches, bacon, apple butter, coffee. We will eat standing up because it is more comfortable.

"It was cold last night. I awoke about one o'clock to pull up the tarp, and saw Orion with his sword chasing the Pleiades across the heavens. Who was it said, 'No Chaldean shepherd or Texas cowboy ever suffered from delusions of grandeur?' Are we but the denizens of a second-rate planet revolving around a fourth-rate and moribund star? The Psalmist said, 'When I consider thy heavens—What is man?' Who may know?

"Last night after dark we all went up on a high point above the camp and set fire to a bunch of dead yucca and sotol stalks. The flames leaped thirty feet into the air. We had promised the superintendent at the camp that we would build a fire on top of Dead Horse Mountains Sunday night. It might have been seen forty miles, and when we see him later in the day, we'll ask him if he saw it.

"Here comes the 'caviya' with Juan behind, carrying the hobbles over his arm. It takes about an hour to pack out. These cowboys use the adverb 'out' in all sorts of ways. We water out the horses, top out the trail, and ride out the country. It's time to roll the bed and help tie it on Brownie.

"This is one of the best pack-train trips I ever took. Yes, I'm tired, sore, and stiff, and have discovered certain bones and muscles I'd forgotten, but, oh, the fun! Just now the fourth day out when one is beginning to get toughened to the saddle and able to sit down at meals, the trip is nearly over. I'll not deny that it will feel good to take off my trousers to sleep, and a shave will doubtless improve my appearance, but I've enjoyed every minute.

Monday Noon

"Well, we're down. Six miles as the crow flies, but we're not crows. We twisted and wiggled and back-tracked down and always down, for ten miles, every step on a rock. Down a dip slope nearly all the way, and across a fault plane. Plenty of slick rock. Waddy advised getting off and walking over the worst places. 'Better climb off les'n you all want to break a laig and have to be packed out.' Our last camp is at Roy's tank, where the truck is to meet us. It hasn't rained for several weeks and there's not much water left in the tank, and pretty thick, too, but the horses didn't mind. Anyhow, it is wet and we will boil it for coffee, so who cares? We still have some Rio Grande water in the canteens for drinking.

"On a trip like this, one gets down to elementals. Water, food, shade, rest, sleep, nothing else matters. We have traveled about seventy miles and have not seen a cow, horse, goat, or human being, except those in our outfit. Four deer, all near the river; a javelina, two road-runners, a few rabbits, and ground squirrels, plenty of quail, doves, and mocking birds. We saw beaver sign on the Rio Grande, and sign of badger, skunk, gopher, and coyote on the trail.

264

"The last meal in camp. No change in the menu. Juan was paid off and started to Boquillas on 'Mulla,' his big hat, the last thing we saw of him, bobbing down the trail. Waddy and Wade will drive the horses across the country to Waddy's ranch, twenty miles away. The truck will take the rest of us to camp, forty miles by road.

At Camp 7:30 p.m.

"The truck was on time. We arrived at camp at 4:30. Bathed, changed, shaved and sat down to supper. Back to civilization— so called—and into the treadmill again. The fun is over. Even if I have passed my seventieth birthday I would like to take such a trip once a month, for that's living."

The five years spent with the National Park Service were busy and profitable years. In a sense these years may be said to represent the culmination of my life's work. I was able to extend my observation and research into areas which, to me, had been unknown.

Not the least of the pleasures of the period which stick in my memory were the friendships I was privileged to make. I count among my best friends some of the people in the regional office at Santa Fé, especially those on the technical staff, and the superintendents and technicians of the various parks and monuments in eight states. Almost without exception I found them to be honest, enthusiastic, industrious men, working together for the common good.

There was my old friend Jesse Nusbaum, for many years superintendent of Mesa Verde National Monument, now senior archaeologist of the service, attached to the Regional Office at Santa Fé. There was W. B. McDougall, the plant ecologist, wild-life technician of the region, with whom I covered so many thousand miles in an automobile. There was Ross Maxwell, my successor as regional geologist, whom I brought fresh from Northwestern University to the Big Bend country in 1936, and whom I love almost as a son. There was Jack Diehl, chief engineer, and a dozen others in the regional office. But as I think of the men whom I met while in the service, two figures stand out, Frank Pinkley and Zeke Johnson, both strong, virile types of self-made Westerners.

For many years Frank Pinkley had been superintendent of Southwestern Monuments with headquarters at Casa Grande Ruin, near Coolidge, Arizona. Pinkley was a very unusual, farsighted man, a good administrator and a good friend. He was generally acknowledged to be the best-loved man in the service in all the Southwest. To his men he was known affectionately as the Boss. He had in a marked degree the ability to string words together, and his articles in the *Southwestern Monument Monthly Report* are examples of clear, cogent English. His untimely death, in 1939, of a heart attack just as he had finished an address of welcome at a conference of his custodians, was mourned by all his friends in the service, and by hundreds of others in Arizona.

Zeke Johnson, a Mormon elder, had been custodian at Natural Bridges National Monument in southeastern Utah for many years. This monument which was set aside by Theodore Roosevelt, includes three magnificent natural bridges, carved by Nature's tools out of massive sandstone. Up until a few years ago the only way for a party to reach the monument was by pack train. But a fairly good auto road has been built, so that one now leaves the highway at the little Mormon town of Blanding, Utah, and drives west fifty miles to the end of the road, where, in a piñon-juniper thicket, he suddenly comes on a tent. This was Zeke's summer home and the headquarters of

266

the monument, and unless he was out on the trail with a party, you would probably find him waiting for you.

Zeke is a tall, rangy youth of some seventy years. The three bridges which form the attraction on the monument are located three miles apart, and the only way to reach them is on foot, which means a nine-mile tramp through brush and sand. Zeke usually makes the trip twice a day.

And Zeke is a singer, with a strong baritone voice, which echoes and re-echoes through the timber and across the mesas, reverberating from cliff to cliff, up and down the canyon. His repertoire is cosmopolitan, ranging from cowboy herd songs to the classics. Zeke knows his West and delights in telling tall stories of Indians, army officers, tenderfeet, outlaws, and cattle rustlers. One day I said, "Zeke, have you ever been East?"

"Sure," said he, "twice."

"So?" said I. "Where?"

"Once to Albuquerque and once to Denver," said Zeke.

And this is the first verse of the robustious song that Zeke sang on the trail the last time we were tramping together down White Rock Canyon. When we got back to the tent after the strenuous nine-mile hike I had Zeke repeat it while I wrote it down.

I was born almost ten thousand years ago,
And there's nothin' in the world that I don't know;
I saw Peter, Paul, and Moses,
Playing ring-around-the-roses
And I'm here to lick the guy what says it isn't so.

In February, 1940, I resigned from the Park Service. Dr. Ross A. Maxwell, who took my place as regional geologist, is now superintendent of Big Bend National Park and the youngest superintendent in the service. I am nearly eighty years old and still average reading a book a day.

Each summer I drive to Canada and spend some happy months with Lois and Ralph and their three children, Charles, Maida, and Linda. I also visit Don and Frances and the two boys, Allen and Warren, in Colorado Springs. I always plan to spend a few weeks in the cabin in South Park that Nina and I built in 1919.

And so ends the story of the Ohio country boy who was born in a log cabin, lived in a dugout in Kansas, and who on a hot August night fifty-seven years ago received his inspiration from a geologist who held up before a roomful of country school teachers two slabs of red sandstone.

INDEX

Adams, George I.: 103
Agassiz, Louis: and story of class notes, 132–33
Alva, Okla.: 80 ff.
Amarillo, Texas: 191, 196; organization of oil company in, 192; discovery of oil near, 193; helium found near, 194–95; growth of, 197; branch office at, 202
Amarillo Oil Co.: 192 ff.
American Mining Congress: meeting of, 138
Amos, F. S. E.: 102
Anderson, G. E.: 217
Anticlines: vi, 110–11, 184, 191; at Dexter, Kan., 51; theory of, 178; at Cornish, Okla., 183; and gas, 185 f.; in Texas Panhandle, 190; interest in, 191; Bravo Dome, 194
Arbuckle Mountains (Okla.): 106, 148, 160; description of, 112; classes visit, 112 ff.; trips to, 114–16; geology of, 158–59; field work in, 169; study of, 170–71; visit of European geologist to, 228–29; examined as site for national park, 242–43
Ashland, Kan.: collecting fossils near, 54
Asp, Henry E.: 74
Athenian Literary Society: 44, 59
Augusta, Kan.: oil field, vi–vii; gas wells near, 185 f.

Baltimore, Md.: 130–31
Bandelier National Monument: cliff dwellings in, 241
Band of Hope, The (temperance society): 21
Barbed wire: story of, 187
Barbour, Erwin H.: 54, 69 f., 129
Barbour, Kate: 103
Barde, Fred S.: 92
Bartlesville, Okla.: 185 f.
Bats: 86–87